ALIVE AND FAT AND THINNING IN AMERICA

Books by Theodore Isaac Rubin

JORDI
LISA AND DAVID
IN THE LIFE
SWEET DADDY
CAT
PLATZO AND THE MEXICAN PONY RIDER
THE TWENTY-NINTH SUMMER
COMING OUT
THE WINNER'S NOTEBOOK
THE THIN BOOK BY A FORMERLY FAT PSYCHIATRIST
THE ANGRY BOOK
EMERGENCY ROOM DIARY
FOREVER THIN
SHRINK!
DR. RUBIN, PLEASE MAKE ME HAPPY
COMPASSION AND SELF-HATE
LOVE ME, LOVE MY FOOL
REFLECTIONS IN A GOLDFISH TANK
UNDERSTANDING YOUR MAN
ALIVE AND FAT AND THINNING IN AMERICA

ALIVE AND FAT AND THINNING IN AMERICA

THEODORE ISAAC RUBIN, M.D.

Coward, McCann & Geoghegan, Inc.
New York

Copyright © 1978 by El-Ted Rubin, Inc.

All rights reserved. This book, or parts thereof, may not be reproduced in any form without permission in writing from the publisher. Published on the same day in Canada by Longman Canada Limited, Toronto.

Library of Congress Cataloging in Publication Data

Rubin, Theodore Isaac.
    Alive and fat and thinning in America.

    1. Reducing. 2. Obesity—Psychological aspects.
3. Body image. I. Title.
RM222.2.R82   6.13.2'5   78-2006

SBN: 698-10915-5

Second Impression

Printed in the United States of America

For Ellie Jacob, Helen, Gene, Florence, Morty,
Oscar, Seth, Steve, and all of us who love to eat.

*'Tis not the meat, but 'tis the appetite
makes eating a delight.*

—Sir John Suckling
"Of Thee, Kind Boy"

Preface

In *The Thin Book By a Formerly Fat Psychiatrist*
I detailed a program of how to prepare oneself psychologically to lose weight.

In *Forever Thin* I discussed the psychodynamics
of obesity.

Alive and Fat and Thinning in America describes
the state of being a fat person in our culture and the
insights necessary to thinning—losing weight and
sustaining weight loss.

Naturally, there is some overlapping of material.
Some of my earlier beliefs have been extended or
modified, and indeed, some of my insights and opinions have changed radically. A number of things I
have learned over the last several years I feel are
very important to a compassionate approach to being fat and, if one so chooses, to getting thin.

11

Introduction

Fat people in our society are made to hate themselves. Hating themselves leads to overeating, gaining weight, and more self-hate. It is virtually impossible to sustain thinness while you are hating yourself, thus an impossible and extremely destructive double bind exists. Fat people are subjected to all kinds of misinformation about fatness and thinness and this, too, is highly demoralizing and destructive. Much of this misinformation is the result of a lack of knowledge of the psychology or emotional dynamics of fat people.

For the most part I use the term *fat* because it tells it like it is. Words like *heavy* and *large* and *stout* are euphemisms, and I feel there is no point in dodging the issue. I like the term fat, and I think other people

13

will like it, too, once its pejorative connotation is removed.

The first part of this book—"Fat and Alive"—describes what it is like to be alive and fat in America. It deals with what I call the "fat" frame of mind and the "thin" frame of mind. I think the reader is in for some surprises. The book largely concerns itself with the vast number of people I call "normally fat," but some of the conditions and dynamics described also apply to severe food addicts and those people who are "malignantly overweight" (more than sixty pounds overweight) or to those people who suffer from illnesses complicated by obesity. The first part of the book is organized in a question and answer format.

The second part—"Thinning"—describes how to be successful in retaining all the advantages of a fat frame of mind while losing weight. Thinning comprises two processes: 1) Losing weight and 2) Sustaining weight loss. The latter is much more difficult. Just about no diet is ever successful unless the individual involved understands the underlying emotional dynamics. I do discuss a diet I consider most reasonable and practical in this section, but thinning is virtually impossible (and for our purposes thinning always includes step two as well as one) without a clear understanding of the dynamics related to the subject. These dynamics are described in "fifteen insights" which make up the second half of the book. After the insights I discuss how I feel about getting outside help.

ONE

Fat and Alive

Let me begin by interviewing myself. I think this may be the shortest route to the heart of the problem. As you may know from my other books, fatness is not alien to me. In an effort to understand myself, other people, and the whole problem of fatness and thinness, I've asked myself these questions again and again. Many other people have asked me these questions too. These are my answers.

Are you fat?

Yes and no. I'm currently thin by most definitions. I'm 6'3", large framed, 54 years old, and I weigh 185 pounds—no clothes. But I have also been fat by any definition. Twenty years ago I weighed 260 pounds and have had difficulty staying thin for most of my adult life. Regardless of what my weight happened to be I have had a "fat man's psychology" all my life. In my head, heart, and soul I am still, and always will be, a fat man.

With rare exceptions I have just about always had a huge appetite. Even as a relatively thin child and adolescent, I loved food and ate accordingly. I remember eating eight lamb chops and sometimes as many as ten and twelve during a "normal" dinner. When I was about twenty-two, my weight shot up considerably beyond that recommended by doctors and insurance charts. It is still a big struggle to cope with what seems like a small amount of food and a continuing formidable appetite.

Is your own fat history the main source of your expertise?

Yes, I think it is my main source, but it is not my only source. The subject has interested me for many years. I remember the "special treatment" accorded fat people when I was a child, and being unable to understand why fat children and adults were the object of ridicule. Years later, I could not agree with the idea that in every fat man there is a thin man trying to get out. Some time ago I began to pick up evidence that many thin people would really like to be

18

fat. Much prejudice is based on envy. This intrigued me. What could "true thins" envy? I investigated this envy in several true thin patients and it became evident that they wanted more than weight gain. "Gusto," "exuberance," "an appetite for life," and other terms and phrases came up providing interesting and important clues. Having been psychoanalysed and being a psychoanalyst myself put me in an advantageous position to understand myself and my fatness, and since we all share common experiences, something of other peoples' problems, too.

So I have for many years researched fatness and its ramifications and have also had a good deal of clinical experience with fat people in my practice. I have treated fat people both individually and in groups. I've also had the benefit of experience gleaned from having served as chief of the obesity section of the Karen Horney Clinic for a number of years. I've written two other books on the subject and have lectured extensively.

How many people in the United States are fat?

Much depends on your definition of "fat." Some people don't feel a person is fat unless he is grossly overweight. Others feel that fatness is defined by their being able to pinch extra skin over the rib cage. I define being physically "fat" as being overweight in terms of ordinary insurance charts and in terms of having great appetite, great interest in food and eating, enough to sustain being overweight. It is very difficult to get exact figures in terms of any definition. But after questioning many kinds of "experts" and doing considerable research, I think that my definition of "fat" would apply to at least half the population. This is a conservative estimate because a number of experts believe that at any given time, more than half the population is "fat." Of course there are a vast number of people who are always losing and gaining weight, and this further complicates the picture. From my point of view nearly all the life-long dieters in the latter group are fat. But by "fat," I mean much more than overweight.

Then you still hold to your "obese profile" described in your book Forever Thin?

Yes, I do! Fat people are mouth and food-oriented people. Food occupies a major part of their minds, feelings, time, and activity. The psychology or psychodynamics which keep people fat described in *Forever Thin* still hold. But that psychological profile: relative passivity, self-effacement, conformity, poor anxiety tolerance, difficulty with anger, distortions of both the psychological and physical image of oneself, and so many other characteristics exist in a great many other people who have never been fat, will never be fat, and who are not at all food-oriented. Some have even been brought up in food-oriented households indistinguishable in this regard from those of fat people. *But* despite almost identical backgrounds vis à vis food and despite having had the same number of fat relatives (parents included), some people go on to become fat people (with or without intermittent periods of thinness) while others are and remain "true thins." I believe that the true thins have important personality differences and I consider these differences vital to our discussion, but I'll get back to this a bit later on.

Then, are you in effect saying we really don't know why people are fat?

We don't know everything, but we do know a lot, and there's more of what I think we ought to know in this small book. Of course, people's weights are directly proportional to how much they eat and the energy they put out. There's no way to get around that. Later I will share with you more of my beliefs about people who sustain fatness and who are, in that sense, different from their thin brothers and sisters.

Unfortunately, the major interest in overweight has been almost purely in its physical aspects. Very few physicians, indeed hardly any at all, have been interested in the psychology involved. This, from my point of view, provides extremely limited information, because understanding the emotional dynamics underlying overweight is absolutely vital to any real insight regarding its control. Being thin or being fat is directly related to eating, but food intake determining fatness or thinness is always the result of a person's particular kind of personality. Ignoring personality information makes for research of the most superficial, shallow, and limited kind.

In The Thin Book by a Formerly Fat Psychiatrist *you said that people who are at all overweight are sick. Do you still believe this?*

This is one of my previous views with which I now take issue. I do not believe the fat half of the population is sicker than the thin half, either physically or psychologically. Of course, I am not including people who are enormously overweight and who are severe food addicts. But ordinarily overweight people are no sicker psychologically or physically than thin people. I feel that my earlier views in this regard were due largely to my own unconscious prejudice against myself and other fat people. Like everyone else, I find it necessary to be careful not to succumb unwittingly to cultural pressures and prejudices—and prejudices are particularly abundant when it comes to fat people.

22

But doesn't fatness lead to all kinds of physical illness and complications?

There are several important points to make in this connection: The role of fatness in physical illness has been ruthlessly exaggerated. Unfortunately, some doctors (whether consciously aware of it or not) use terror tactics with their patients, dramatizing the dire consequences of overweight, without adequate proof or rationale, in order to pressure them to lose weight. Of course being 200 pounds overweight is highly destructive, but no more so than being severely underweight. There is simply no proof that ordinary fatness plays a significant role in human disease.

Different people have different predilections, physical as well as psychological. People brought up differently reflect this in their approach to food; often their attitudes are determined by ethnic or regional familiarity. Radically altering food habits can be more destructive than continuation of habits whose roots have been planted in infancy. Many physicians feel that constant fluctuation—that is, losing and gaining weight over and over again or the so-called "yo-yo" syndrome—is much more destructive than sustained overweight. People do not apparently do well when they are required to make a great many adaptations. I feel that undue stress generated by stringent pressure to diet and lose weight is often more destructive emotionally, and eventually physically, than the weight itself. I have seen entirely too many people in consultation who generated enormous self-hate whenever they either failed to lose weight or gained a few pounds. One very depressed man I saw recently turned out to have a rare glandular disturbance. His efforts to lose weight were futile, and as a result, he felt that he was a "failure," "no good," and so on. Although his case and other cases of endocrinological disturbance are rare, self-hate following pressure from oneself or others to lose weight is not rare. Self-hate produces more eating, more self-hate, and more stress and is destructive to both one's emotional and physical well-being.

Are you saying that being fat does not affect one's physical health?

How fat or *how* overweight is the significant question here. It is possible for a person to be so fat that he is unable to breathe lying down. I had one patient who was almost 300 pounds overweight. As she gained weight over the years, she went from a reclining to an almost upright position when she slept. As she lost weight she was able gradually to discard all kinds of upright supports she had devised. Happily, she is now normally heavy and can sleep prone with just an ordinary pillow. Being grossly overweight is especially destructive to people who tend to be diabetic or who suffer from hypertension. *But* the role of fatness and what has come to be called fatness in our society has been greatly exaggerated, confused and over-simplified.

I think one of the worst misconceptions we hold to is that between what we eat and fatness. Some thin, truly thin people eat very little and relatively seldom, but they eat foods consisting mainly of cholesterol and polyglycerides as well as a great deal of caffeine. Some fat people eat much and relatively often, but they eat foods that are healthier in terms of their effect on arteries and organs generally.

Physical differences are important in determining fat. The kind of frame one has in terms of dimension and bone density is relevant. And a person's metabolism, the rate at which he burns up food is also significant. The kind of work a person does in terms of amount of exercise and energy-expenditure is important. Age and climate also play a role. Very active people in cold climates who do not eat enough and lose weight (the polar Eskimo) and who have a history of limited exposure to infectious diseases may be prone to serious illness—malignant forms of measles, tuberculosis, and so on. Fat people who have the same dimensions and the same weight may have great differences in blood cholesterol, tissue fat, muscular development, tone of muscles and skin. Weight loss may be indicated for one and not for another. The history of a person's physical health, his eating habits, and his weight levels over a lifetime are very important in evaluating potential effects of significant weight change. Radical weight loss, even over an extended period of time, is not always constructive. Sometimes it can be harmful physically and catastrophic psychologically. Human beings are complex creatures and being fat is itself a complicated extension of this. The blanket dictum that being fat is bad for physical health while being thin is good is a vast oversimplification that has a considerable potential for harm.

Do you feel that doctors are prejudiced in terms of fatness and health?

Absolutely! Who are doctors? They are people and unless they lead unusually encapsulated lives they are inevitably influenced as much by cultural pressures, conventions, and styles as anyone else. Doctors are no more immune than anyone else to the influences of propaganda, both blatant and subtle. I think a great many doctors who are fat themselves are full of self-hate and, without conscious awareness, project much of their own feelings to their fat patients whom they evaluate and treat with considerable prejudice—even outright dislike and contempt. You see, doctors (and as I indicated earlier, myself included) are as much the victims of cultural prejudice as the patients they victimize. The difficul-

26

ty here is that the doctor does not *know* that he is prejudiced. This is particularly destructive in terms of his judgment of his fat patients. Indeed, many doctors may pride themselves on a lack of prejudice when quite the opposite is true. This may mitigate against sound medical judgment. Therefore, full conscious awareness of prejudice on the physician's part is already a giant step forward in his being able to bring sound clinical judgment to bear on the subject in general, as well as on the particular treatment of any individual.

One of my patients who is a physician found his work with fat people far more effective after we had worked on a prejudice he was unaware he had. Part of our work revealed his hatred for himself as a fat child, hatred he had almost completely repressed. He is currently thin but, in treatment, he eventually admitted to a great fear of fatness, which it turned out was connected to his unhappy childhood and rejection by his peers during that time in his life.

How do doctors victimize fat people?

Some victimization boils down to obvious, conscious, self-serving charlatanry and chicanery, much of which is, unfortunately, economically determined. There is an increasing number of so-called doctors who run weight-reduction mills and inflict on their innocent victims all kinds of extreme, fad, and inappropriate diets. Hazardous as these diets are, these people are quick to dispense useless and dangerous drugs and bizarre and noxious food substitutes. Weight reduction has become an ugly, multimillion dollar business, both inside and outside the confines of established medicine. There is an ever-increasing number of "spas," "health farms," "gyms" and so on dedicated to making money from fat people. This is not to say there aren't good facilities, but many of these businesses are utterly ruthless in their lack of concern for their clients' welfare.

My main concern in this connection is the legitimate, and even well-meaning, qualified doctor. Many of them are prejudiced against fat people, and this prejudice exists in both thin and fat doctors. It takes various forms; some, in the process of exaggerating the danger of fatness, become so obsessed with fat that they neglect and even overlook other important medical problems. Others, viewing a fat person, cannot see beyond the fatness—fatness is all they subsequently see relative to that person. The fat patient is lumped together with a general population of other fat people in the doctor's mind and practice and, in effect, loses his medical individuality and identity. Some doctors, even while viewing fat patients with distaste and loss of medical interest, simply become resigned to the condition and abandon any effort to encourage weight reduction. Others become overzealous, even sadistic and vindictive, producing weight-obsessed patients who become guilt-

28

ridden, masochistic and obsessed with their condition. Depression and anxiety are not unusual in
these victimized patients, and complications due to
such depression and anxiety are often misinterpret-
ed as being provoked by fatness. This produces
more guilt and anxiety, completing a disastrous vi-
cious cycle. In many cases doctors and their fat patients form sado-masochistic relationships that go
on for years without conscious awareness on either
side of the role each one is playing in this destructive drama.

*Are you saying, then, that society is generally prej-
udiced against fat people and that doctors are an extension or reflection of this prejudice?*

Yes, but it's more than a prejudice. It's a national
obsession! Many people do not know how they will
feel during the day until they weigh themselves in
the morning. They've reached the point where their
moods, feelings, and level of self-acceptance are entirely and directly predicated on weight level. And
for many people this level is based on a cruel standard of extreme thinness. When spontaneity gives
way to such compulsion that a scale determines
mood, we know we have reached a state of serious
and destructive national obsession. A patient of
mine recently told me how she discovered that she
walks differently depending upon what her scale

reads each day. If she is *down* a pound or two, her walk will be "bouncy," "youthful," and "proud." If she is *up* a pound, her walk will be "draggy," "slow," "old" and "worn out."

But what of other prejudices? Fat people are made to look dowdy and ridiculous by clothing manufacturers who know they will gratefully buy anything at all that fits, because there's nothing stylish made for them to choose from. Fashion designers will either scorn or simply ignore them. In our country advertisers consistently use models who are not only thin but often severely underweight. Various aids to thinning are constantly promoted in newspapers and magazines with little or no regard for their efficacy. On television and in films, fat people are still used in subservient and comic roles, reinforcing the general notion that fatness is dumb, disgusting, and contemptible, while thinness is smart, beautiful, and a passport to total acceptance. And this prejudice extends into every area of living.

In one instance, a patient told me that she was having a business conversation with her lawyer one afternoon when he suddenly interrupted her, asking, "Why don't you lose weight?" Since their relationship was formal and professional, she felt he was being both presumptuous and inappropriate. However, the incident did not surprise her because it was not the first time someone had taken unusual and personal license, simply because she was fat. As I've said, prejudice exists on just about all levels. As a matter of fact these days prejudice against fat people virtually transcends and supersedes all other prejudices, including those against race, ethnic group, and sexual identification. And more important, there is generally more compassion for just about any other group of people—and this includes alcoholics, drug addicts, sex offenders, and criminals—than there is for the fat. Prejudice against fat people exists in social situations, in employment practices, and in college admission procedures. On a far more subtle level, fat people are simply not taken seriously in any area of living. Either their individuality is completely ignored—"You know who I mean, that fat guy"—or they are treated with out-and-out contempt and sometimes ridicule. Even children can be guilty of it, unconsciously acting out the feelings of their parents. Some have already been directly influenced by the society they live in. I saw a fat woman in consultation recently, who told me that she had gone to her ten-year-old son's school for "Open School Week." When he saw her, her son, who was with some friends and teachers, turned his head away. Later on she told him she hoped she did not embarrass him. This ordinarily loving, concerned, and sensitive child said, "You didn't. When they asked me who you were, I said you were the lady who lived next door."

31

What are the origins of fat prejudice?

I'm not at all sure. It undoubtedly has multiple
roots. The biblical injunction against gluttony, the
fashion trends of this particular era, preoccupation
of the media with diet, overzealous doctors—all play
a role. Once this sort of attitude gets set in motion,
roots are no longer necessary. It becomes autonomous and is there because it's there and gives itself
life as it continues to be there. This is always true of
manifestations that are largely part of unconscious
processes. You see, many people are unaware of
their prejudice. But this, if anything, makes it worse.
Unconscious bigotry is even stronger and more pervasive than the conscious variety, and often takes
subtle but insidious destructive forms. Perhaps one
kind of prejudice comes from envy of thin people
who perceive fat people as capable of greater exuberance and vitality than they are. But let's talk
about that later on. People dividing themselves
against each other for all kinds of dubious reasons—
race, color, sexual preference, and so on—provide
ample precedence for discrimination and hostility
based on nothing more than difference in weight.
Prejudice requires no special logic or rationale other
than the need to construct a fantasy hierarchy to fool
somebody into believing that he or she is better than
or superior to someone else. I should say that, being
part of the culture, many fat people themselves are
also prejudiced and come to respect thin people un-

duly, while hating themselves and other fat people who remind them of themselves.

I saw this dramatically demonstrated in a therapy group a few years ago. Several fat people were absolutely in awe of two very thin group members for no reason other than that they were thin. As one of the fat people became noticeably more thin herself, she became increasingly contemptuous and patronizing of her fat confreres. Without full, conscious awareness she did her best to disassociate herself from them. These attitudes, and especially the projected self-hate, were eventually worked out and ameliorated in the therapeutic situation. But the vast majority of people, fat and thin alike, seldom get the chance to explore, reveal, and change highly destructive attitudes.

Does this prejudice exist all over the world?

It is very much a question of time, place, and I suspect, economic conditions, especially regarding food supply. I doubt that it exists among starving Indians in Calcutta or among hungry South Americans. While starving people may feel envious and hostile to their obviously well-fed compatriots, it is not likely they would relish thinness and be inwardly prejudiced or even disinclined toward fatness. On the contrary, in many cultures fatness is actually a condition to which one aspires since it may be seen as both evidence and a symbol of substance, accomplishment, and influence. I remember one fat woman I was seeing in treatment who came back from a trip to Mexico astounded that men there found her very attractive and her "roundness" beauty-enhancing. A friend of mine who is well acquainted with the Middle East recently told me that a big belly in some Arab countries is seen as a mark of substance, wealth, responsibility, and general capability.

It is interesting that the major obsession with thinness (because the obsession is with being *thin* rather than being fat) occurs in our society—where our food supply and general affluence is the greatest in the world. It is almost as if man must find a way to struggle, even if he must go out of his way to construct a value system antithetical to one that represents good fortune.

Interesting, that only a generation or so ago people came here from all over the world to avoid starvation. And some continued to starve here too. So many died of tuberculosis aided by malnutrition in the early nineteen hundreds. Wasn't it natural that those people and their descendants, given a healthy desire for life, would identify life with food and good appetite and eat accordingly? Isn't it interesting, too, that if poor people saw food, eating, and fatness as salvation that rich people would then have to adopt thinness as a standard to help differentiate them from the lowly hordes? But even in this country it wasn't that long ago that plumpness was

identified with health and even sexual attractiveness. Even being fat did not preclude sex appeal.
But it is especially true of Americans to polarize and
quickly veer in the direction of extremes. As soon as
thinness became a virtue and was backed by fashion
and media pundits, everyone rallied to its flag with a
vengeance, despite residual large appetites and ves-
tigial memories of times when standards and food
supplies were otherwise.　　2013062

Other countries fail to share our thinness obsession. Standards are not nearly as severe in other
parts of the world, though they may well become so
as further Americanization and homogenization take
place. The American film industry's influence on
style alone is all-pervasive. However, there are still
parts of the world where fatness is not equated with
idiocy or with loss of sex appeal. I already men-
tioned Mexico and the Near East. In Germany, for
example, at least a certain degree of fatness is regarded as expressing honesty, health, and the stuff of po-
litical charisma. Yes, fat candidates make out better
than thin ones, and generally seem to generate more
hope and optimism as they project a sense of *gemüt-
lichkeit* in German voters. As in Mexico, plumpness
in women is seen as attractive, and fat women do not
lack masculine attention. Of course, the examination
of works of art through the ages attest to the change
of styles and give ample evidence to support the fact
that there never has been an absolute esthetic criterion for ideal weight. One only has to think of the

works of Rubens and Renoir to substantiate the role of plumpness in standards of feminine beauty. Even America once equated voluptuousness with beauty; early film stars were worshipped for their abundant curves where today slenderness is an absolute requirement for stardom.

Well, what is it really like to be "alive and fat" in America?

It is pretty grim, and this despite the fact that the fat person often has an enormously constructive outlook.

In our society fatness is directly equated with stupidity, laziness, childishness, foolishness, lack of energy or ordinary motivation, inadequate goal direction, asexuality or lack of sexual drive, vulgarity, insensitivity, coarseness, ignorance, apathy, selfishness, cowardice, and ugliness. And this devastating list goes on and on. These stereotypes are largely felt on an unconscious level, but this in no way mitigates their conscious effect. The fact is that fat people suffer from prejudice of all kinds in almost every human relationship and endeavor they encounter in life.

But not only do they suffer prejudice and ensuing self-hate, they also endure enormous temptation and conflict.

Our country advertises and exploits, for money, every possible benefit for and of thinness. At the same time, and equally aggressively, it advertises, promotes, and demonstrates food, especially fattening junk foods, and its availability. Our society is largely directed to consumerism, acquisitiveness, and the addition of visible signs of substance and goods to ourselves. But it is hands-down against being fat.

Our culture is schizophrenic on this score. Eating in and eating out—all kinds of eating and drinking—is associated with sociability. The ads on television and radio and in newspapers and magazines bombard us with the attractions of potato chips, candy, frankfurters, cheese, hamburgers, pizzas, pasta, and every variety and kind of restaurant and appliance to prepare still more food. At the same time models, actresses, and clothes designers celebrate the absolute virtue of thinness. Indeed, heroic, ideal, desirable, sexy, happy, powerful people are always portrayed in our society as thin. This kind of double and incompatible standard is especially hard on the vulnerable and already self-hating fat person. Its demoralizing effect may or may not be felt consciously, but it is *always* felt and invariably leads to serious repercussions.

The fact is that we are at once a food and thinness-oriented and obsessed society. A good part of our business and social lives are conducted either in restaurants or at dinners in one another's homes. We break bread together, and bread in our country comes in a million tempting forms. This wedding of business and pleasure is particularly difficult for fat people, who are asked to eat, and who have the appetites to do food justice, and who are then discriminated against for eating. In effect, they are punished for not exerting control and curtailing their natural exuberance. I'll have more to say about this later, but I do want to say here that fat people are chronically drawn into deep conflict on this score and must repeatedly suffer the frustration and helplessness characteristic of this dread double bind. From my point of view, a culture which is antithetical to being human is a sick culture. When in effect harsh judgment is meted out to those who eat food which is actively offered, a sick, frustrating, double bind situation inevitably exists. This is antithetical to the human condition and offers ample evidence that change is required.

As I said earlier, fat people are as subject to cultural pressures as thin, and therefore each "failure"— each eating bout or delinquency from the diet— brings on attacks of self-hate, self-doubt, anxiety, and depression. Many fat people view going off a diet as "being bad," while they see resisting food as "being good." This is a self-judgmental form of discrimination that generally overrates and exaggerates the virtues of self-control in all regards.

Fat and Alive

Are you saying, then, that thinness in our culture is equated with self-control?

Yes, I am saying that—that and more. In our culture self-control and the self-censoring of feelings are still further equated with strength, discretion, dignity, logic, clarity of thought, maturity and wisdom. Having feelings and demonstrating them is, on the other hand, associated with weakness and foolishness. Openness and the ready ability to share what one thinks and how one feels are often viewed with suspicion as being strange, if not threatening qualities.

The thin person, on a conscious level, and particularly on an unconscious one, is seen as possessing self-control and a predisposition to being responsible and reliable, while the fat person is seen as having no control in eating, and therefore as potentially chaotic and irresponsible in all areas of life. When fat people turn out otherwise, they are regarded as exceptions and are sometimes viewed with surprise and even bewilderment. ("But he's so fat, how can he be responsible?") If openness and a ready demonstration of feeling is coupled in a particular person with fatness—and that person then reveals obvious ability and evidence of responsibility, much confusion ensues in people who are predisposed to stereotyped thinking.

Then do fat people envy thin people because they think thins have greater self-control? Is this why fat people want to be thin?

This is one of the reasons. Of course the overriding reason is the desire for acceptance and respect. Achieving thinness does indicate to a fat person that an individual has managed self-control concerning eating. He also harbors the unconscious illusion that thinness will automatically bring reserve, general self-control, and the aura of dignity and maturity he thinks is characteristic of people who have relatively little interest in food. Of course this is illusion. New-found self-control over eating is just that and nothing more. New patterns of eating do not alter character structure, and fat people are actually fortunate in this respect. I said that this illusion largely exists on an unconscious level. This makes it particularly powerful since it exerts its influence without dilution of rational logic. Therefore, fat people pursue thinness with the conviction that thinness and the self-control necessary to achieve it will somehow rid them of all self-contempt and concomitant ills, will raise their self-esteem, and will immediately elevate them to a position of worth in society. As I explained in *Forever Thin*—vast expectations of thinness make fat people fear thinness because on another level it also represents unfamiliar and fearful changes they are frightened they will not achieve or be able to sustain. Of course society helps to promote the magic of

40

thinness and the illusions connected to it. Thus, the simultaneous desire and fear of thinness is almost a guarantee of fatness, because the fat person generally responds to fear and anxiety by eating. Also, eating in this case helps keep the fat person fat and "safe" from "change"—safe from the disappointment implicit in getting thin and realizing that no magical change takes place at all.

As for true thins, contrary to what the fat person believes, not eating doesn't represent self-control at all. It is easy and natural for these people not to eat because they simply do not have the appetite. Indeed, it often takes considerable will power and a kind of performance for them to eat with joy and gusto. This reminds me of people lacking a sense of humor who have learned to laugh when everybody else laughs at jokes they don't understand.

Is self-control linked to other characteristics our culture holds in high regard?

Actually, self-control is only part of several characteristics associated with thinness and a character structure more broadly described as "detached." Many true thins are detached, and "thinness" applies both to their feelings about food as well as about self, other people, life and the world in general. (Of course there are some thins who are not "thin" or "detached" in their emotional lives and

41

outlooks, and there are even some who are not even thin in their approach to food. But many of these gregarious thins are pseudo-members of the "true thin" group, have a fat psychology, and have developed control concerning food. I'll say more about them later.) In any case detached people are erroneously seen as having great reserves of strength, mysterious knowledge, and pure objectivity. Of course, the strong and silent "mind your own business, keep to yourself" syndrome has always been highly promoted in our society. The quality of noninvolvement, of being aloof and above the battle—oblivious to all people, concerns, and involvements—has been made part of our popular culture. Consider how immediate our response is to the lure of the loner, the supremacy of intellect, the besieged fortress that never gives way, the freedom from mundane associations—all these and more are touted as being wonderful goals and attributes. The Gary Cooper frontier loner type has been romanticized by our culture for a hundred years.

Of course, self-reliance is all right, but involvement and normal mutual dependency are crucial to survival. A great deal of detachment in men and women is chronic, compulsive, and for the most part, evidence of considerable neurosis. Detachment in these cases is mainly used as a defense against anxiety, fear of people, feelings of poor self-esteem, and extreme inner fragility. It is sometimes accompanied by a deadening of feeling and a sapping of

42

vitality. However, the culture we live in does not take cognizance of the destructive aspects of detachment and continues actively to promote "coolness" and emotional reserve in all areas of life. Perhaps this idealization of detachment is largely a function of the great complexity and pressure with which most of us live. Perhaps withdrawal is felt as the most effective kind of protection against stress. In any case, detachment is probably the most common form of defense against anxiety, feelings of vulnerability, and general insecurity. Probably to a lesser or greater degree, it affects a majority of the population. This of course does not make for happiness. Detachment and deadening of feeling curtails the possibility of self-realization and happiness in both the individual who sustains it and the person and persons with whom he or she has close relationships. It is neither easy nor fruitful to live with a person who refuses to become fully emotionally involved, who remains essentially aloof and apart. And it also promotes in the detached an unconscious envy of people who seem to feel deeply and who are able to express feelings, especially those capable of large appetite and exuberance. This "unconscious" envy often gives rise to conscious resentment and hostility.

The fact is that detached people are often simply resigned, stuck in a "noninvolved," withdrawn stalemate with life. Though they may be envied for what appears to be cultural conformity, and of

43

course, invulnerability, self control, and strength, they are usually, simply put—no fun to be with. Neither stimulating nor giving, they are just not particularly interesting once one's own fantasy about them ceases. Projecting to a blank screen is not especially rewarding and one gets tired of plumbing mysteries and depths that may simply not be there. Attraction is usually to a symbol rather than to a real person who essentially remains hidden. How much of a real person exists is an individual matter. Detachment itself is relative. We are all detached to a certain extent, but many of us use withdrawal as a primary defense, and this largely determines how we behave, especially toward other people. People often form neurotic locks in which relationships are based largely on common neurotic needs—mutual attraction based on neurosis. Thus, fat people and thin people may form neurotic bonds based on idealization of one another's characteristics which each feels is lacking in his and her self.

Are you saying that true thins are detached, and that fat people aren't and are more expansive?

A great many fat people are expansive, and a great many thins are detached. This is not surprising because eating is very often an extension of personality and character structure generally. After all, everything we are and what we do and how we do it is an expression of ourselves. Appetite and eating are no exception. But, of course, there are also expansive thins and detached fats, and all of us have at least some degree of each characteristic. But it is important to realize that many currently thin (in weight) people have a fat outlook, and may indeed have been fat people in the past. In this regard it is important to know a person's history vis à vis food as well as his or her present feelings about eating. True thins simply do not have the same feeling about food as fats or fat-thins. Most simply don't care that much about eating and can virtually take it or leave it. Any enthusiasm on the subject is focused more on an intellectual level than on a practical eating one. They may *talk* recipes, but great gusto in eating is missing, and may well be missing in other areas of their lives as well. We recently went out to dinner with some true thin friends who took us to a place they had raved about. At the table my primary interest was the food. They seemed to enjoy it vicariously through me, asking every few minutes how I felt about this or that dish. They themselves pecked at the food, were easily distracted by other things, and their plates were removed nearly three-quarters full. Needless to say, not so with mine, even though I am *currently thin.*

A former patient of mine, a true thin, is a superb cook but eats very little himself. As his treatment progressed, he invited larger numbers of people to dinner parties he gave. He served his guests graciously and enjoyed their involvement with the food as his involvement with the people themselves increased. On close questioning, he revealed that what delighted him most was the way the food looked. He liked to please his guests with good tasting food, but neither taste nor smell really interested him, and he continued to eat very little. His greatest joy on a personal level was in how the table settings looked and in the design of each dish of food. He actually prepared foods whose colors and shapes went well together on beautifully designed plates. I can readily appreciate the aesthetics of well-displayed food elegantly served. But on a gut level, as a fat man, it is hard for me to see this aspect of food take precedence over its smell and taste.

Of course we cannot expect perfect consistency where human behavior is concerned. There are people who eat expansively but who are otherwise constricted, and there are people who are otherwise expansive but who are constricted where food is concerned. However, appetites—in terms of appetite for life in general, for feeling, for reaching out to others—are often of one pattern and fabric.

Well, do true thins ever enjoy food?

Many true thins eat in order to live, and a handful live in order to eat, but some enjoy food, though not usually in the same full-spirited, whole-hearted way that fat people do. For many true thins it is as difficult to cast aside constraint and constriction when it comes to eating as it is in other areas. Interestingly, many true thins enjoy very hot foods—food so highly spiced that other people can't possibly eat it without enormous discomfort and outright distress. Perhaps, in a compensatory way, only super-spicing can awaken relatively deadened tastes and feelings.

When true thins enjoy food, it is usually in terms of quality rather than quantity. Some true thins go on a binge occasionally and eat a large quantity of food, making everyone wonder how they stay so thin. The answer is simply that a very large meal is usually followed by eating little or nothing for the next few days. I should point out that there are still more gourmet eaters among fats than thins, but fat gourmet eaters usually demand quantity as well as quality.

You talked earlier about fats who are temporarily thin. Are there thins, true thins, who become temporarily fat?

Yes, there are, but they are rare and the fat phase is temporary! It is almost as if these people are trying to break through a solid wall of resignation with a thrust of appetite and eating. This may also be accompanied by appetite and movement in other areas as well (sex, occupation, social interests, and so on). But this surge of exuberance, along with the fatness it may produce, doesn't usually last. And again, one of the distinguishing characteristics of a true thin who goes on a binge is his propensity for spicy foods. This persists even after his temporary food interest has disappeared. Some thin people may even struggle sufficiently hard that they succeed in breaking through a great deal of resignation and continue a more involved and open existence for the rest of their lives. I believe, as Karen Horney did, that all people can grow. But even in these rare cases, intense food interest almost never lasts. Our basic attitude toward food and eating always has a long history whose roots are seldom extricated.

Are you actually saying that overweight in a true thin can be evidence of increased mental health?

We must keep in mind that human beings are the most complicated creatures on earth. Application of oversimplified rules designed to instantly illuminate behavior and motivation often give false information. So, though it sounds strange in the context of our thinness obsessed society that overweight might even be a sign of health, this may nevertheless be true. I am not saying it is always the case. There are times when acute behavior change may be evidence of emotional disturbance, so that each person's behavior patterns must be carefully evaluated on an individual basis, taking into consideration both past history and current status. But yes, I do believe that appetite leading to increased weight and even to overweight may in true thins be a sign of resurgence of feelings, health, and appetite for living and, in this way, may be symbolic of health as well as an extension of movement in a healthy direction.

Is there any special psychological significance in the case of people who are extremely thin?

Indeed there is, and I view both extreme fatness and extreme thinness as psychosomatic disturbances, or diseases if you will. Remember that in ordinary conditions where severe debilitating disease is not present, weight is a function of eating, and how much we eat (and weigh) is largely a function of personality and immediate mood or emotional state. Exaggerated eating practices, either in terms of type or quantity of foods eaten, are inevitably the result of emotional or characterological disorders or both. This applies to both severe undereating as well as overeating and its consequent severe thinness or obesity. The roots of the illness are psychological and are usually connected to unresolved unconscious conflicts producing more than ordinary anxiety. The response to the anxiety is expressed either in overeating or near starvation resulting in gross obesity or severe thinness.

The illness known as *anorexia nervosa* is an extreme form of food deprivation leading to thinness so pronounced it often results in death. It is always a manifestation of severe emotional disturbance and invariably requires the care of both an internist and a psychiatrist. Interestingly, I have seen a number of anorexic people who, at an earlier time in their lives, had been grossly overweight. Their intense and extreme degree of compulsiveness in eating had shifted to noneating. Their obsession with food had shifted to a phobic response against food. These people had virtually no history of moderation vis à vis food. In some cases, the same people demonstrated considerable evidence of lack of moderation in other areas of their lives as well. Some obsessive overeaters were also compulsive in their business activities. Some obsessive food phobics were almost reclusive in their avoidance of business or social contact.

Does current mood play a role in eating?

Yes, in ordinary fats and thins both general personality or character structure and immediate moods affect their current food behavior. Character structure determines the overall food habits and patterns, making the fat, fat and the thin, thin. But their response to immediate mood is also important. I have usually found that fats eat when they are anxious and lose appetite when they are depressed. Thins eat even less than they ordinarily do in a state of anxiety, and still less when they are depressed. The effect of mood on appetite may be blatant or subtle, sudden or go on over an extended period of time. I have seen patients both in and out of institutions gradually and almost imperceptibly withdraw from eating until near starvation occurred. This withdrawal from eating sometimes provides evidence of the onset of severe depression, long before other clinical signs manifest themselves. I had one patient who initially experienced loss of appetite with reduced salivary gland output ("I have such a dry mouth") which was always followed by much anxiety and agitation. A return of appetite and normal salivary output preceded her return to a more comfortable emotional state.

Can not-eating bring on depression in fat people?

This is an extremely important question, the answer to which any fat person contemplating serious dieting should understand.

Many fats are susceptible to depression when they change their eating habits and lose weight. There are at least several factors that play a role here. First, there is a general curtailment and sometimes actual deprivation (in stringent diets) of a primary enjoyment. Eating is primary in any hierarchy of enjoyment in fat people. This means exactly what it says—that eating ranks first among the pleasurable possibilities that exist in a fat person's world. Curtailment of eating, let alone severe deprivation, removes this source of pleasure and even more, also destroys *anticipation* of pleasure—and warmth. This is so because fat people spend a great deal of time enjoying the anticipation of eating and also experience both the anticipation and the eating itself as a warm, loving experience. In fact eating and meals also represent the most effective way they have of dividing time.

This means that meals and food and anticipation of food are both unconsciously and consciously their way of feeling out the time of day—actually the time of their lives. This process of dividing time into the day and the week by the anticipation of meals and of eating (chicken on Friday, eating out Saturday) has strong association of both food and place and is further accentuated by the conviviality involved in eating among fats. For them it is usually a highly social, convivial, sharing experience (with the exception of severely overweight, reclusive eaters). Breaking bread together has very real and highly symbolic value for fat people. Eating is looked forward to as an experience where food, talk, and feelings are exchanged and shared. This kind of breaking up of time in terms of eating meals takes place in thins, too, but not nearly with the same deep meaning, let alone pleasurable anticipation. The fact is that thins often forget about meals altogether. Fats never forget. Thins, also, often disassociate eating from socializing and generally do not experience eating and food in the richly symbolic way that fats do. Therefore, fats often become depressed in dieting because, in giving up food, they are also surrendering happy anticipation, social exchange, warmth, sharing, love, and the general sense of well-being and comfort they feel while sitting at a dinner table. Sometimes in dieting fats also experience a sense of disorientation. This is due in part to the change in eating routine and is especially pronounced if the diet calls for actually missing meals. As I've indicated, the fat person's most significant clock is his meal times. Altering meal routine as well as changing menu produce a disorienting jolt.

And dieting has another dislocating effect in terms of our sense of self or our feeling of substantiality. Let me explain. Fat people experience their largeness—and largeness of feelings generally—through their physical selves. They are much in touch with their sensations and of course experience their sensations through their bodies. This means that feelings in general are more closely integrated with a sense of body proportions than is so in their thin confreres. While a sense of vanity in terms of cultural standards may be missing, they are nevertheless very much "body aware people." This means that they experience their own substantiality through their bodies, and adding food and weight is both symbolic and actual in contributing to that sense of substantiality. Fatness may cause self-hate when subjected to cultural standards of acceptance. *But* not eating and loss of weight may cause self-hate, since it may well be felt as a depleting and detracting process in terms of personal substantiality. This psychological dynamic is intensified if the fat person comes from a family whose history includes food deprivation and who consequently put a great deal of emphasis on the power and security afforded by food and eating. Obviously, this kind of personal dynamic linking a sense of substantiality, strength, and health to eating makes for a powerful conflict when set against the cultural demand for dieting and thinness. Depression and anxiety thus come from two sources. The feeling that one is promoting insubstantiality causes depression, and the feeling of being pulled apart by conflict causes both anxiety *and* depression. If the depression is mild, the fat person will often eat to overcome the anxiety of the conflict and to help repress the entire untenable set of incompatible dynamics. But if the depression is strong enough, the fat person may lose his or her appetite. A total loss of appetite is a very serious sign of potential deep depression in a fat person and may indicate the need for analytic treatment.

This, then, brings us to the third major cause of

depression in fat people who lose weight. Obviously, if eating and fatness is a defense against depression and anxiety, then removing that barrier may
well involve experiencing those moods and feelings
the fat person has used food to defend against. Few
of us welcome a change in status quo either in the
image we have of ourselves or in any aspect of our
lifestyles. Most of us abhor the unfamiliar, and this is
true even when the familiar or status quo is a painful
one. Psychiatrists often encounter this phenomenon
in dealing with chronic depression. The patient
wants to feel better but is afraid to surrender *familiar* feelings of depression. Fat people are afraid to
give up overeating (and a familiar body image) as a
defense against anxiety. As I've written elsewhere,
they are also afraid of thinness because thinness
represents all sorts of threatening expectations of
self and of life generally, many of them unrealistic.
But not eating and the possibility of consequent
thinness also feels to the fat person like the beginning of the end to an entire lifestyle—and this is indeed threatening. The surrender of food represents
the surrender of one's whole "fat psychology," and
it is the possibility of this loss which is most anxiety
producing and which accounts for increased defen-
sive eating. Of course, this "fat psychology" is very
important to our understanding of the food personality situation, but before we go further into that,
there are still a few preliminary questions to answer.

Is eating the only defense fat people have in response to anxiety?

It's a major response. Of course fat people have all the character defense responses everyone else has—including rationalization, compartmentalization, illusion, phobias, projection, displacement, and so on. But they also tend to talk more and to become more sexually active in times of anxiety. In general they tend to reach out—unlike thins who tend to withdraw in response to anxiety. Fat people are usually givers and takers. They are "people people," or in other words, they *need* people, especially during difficult times. Often, even in deep depression, fat people grow restless and agitated and are sometimes eager to share symptoms and life histories with whomever is present. Thins, on the other hand, often become withdrawn, silent, and self-contemplative in the same circumstances. Fat people in therapy will often ask for reassurance and support and, if they don't get it, will sometimes exaggerate their pain and symptoms to the point of hysteria in an attempt to manipulate their therapists. Withdrawal from food, people, communication, and so on in fat people is often evidence of imminent emotional disturbance (depression) of severe proportions.

Fat and Alive

Are fat people generally more subject to depression than thins?

Fat people are capable of mood fluctuations. They are usually very much in touch with, or at least close to, their feelings, and they also feel intensely. This, combined with the need to reach out to others, makes all their moods more apparent to those around them, and they are moody people.They are also highly reactive people. This means that they are strongly affected by other people and are capable of feeling the whole range of emotions from love to rage vis à vis others. Since fat people usually have a great need to feel liked by others, they often have great difficulty with anger. As I explained in other books, they repress much anger with the help of eating. Food binges are often anger equivalents. Instead of showing anger, which may incur other people's disfavor, they eat and overeat. This almost always happens on an unconscious level. Making their anger conscious and experiential—in other words, feeling it—is crucial in sustaining weight loss.

I'll have more to say about this in the second half of the book. But in answer to the question of depression, yes, fat people have, I believe, a greater potential for depression, just as I believe that thin people have a great potential for withdrawal. One can argue that depression is a form of withdrawal. But this is not true. People can be withdrawn with and without depression, and they can be depressed with and without withdrawal. Indeed, thin people usually go through a relatively quiet and deadening kind of depression when they get depressed. Fat people, on the other hand, often suffer from agitated depressions characterized by tension and movement, as well as hysteria, sleeplessness, and general agitation. Even in the most depressed states, fat people usually seek out others and are often more talkative (in seeking help) than when they feel well.

From my point of view, our population is about equally divided into those who tend toward withdrawal and those who tend toward cyclic mood swings. When they are very sick, the withdrawn half tends toward schizoid and schizophrenic reactions. The mood swingers in heavy sickness tend to have manic-depressive reactions.

Can over-eating cause depression in thin people?

Before I answer this question, let me remind you again that true thins who suddenly and radically alter food habits may be demonstrating considerable emotional disturbance and severe inner conflict. This is especially true of people who become obese and who, for the first time in their adult life, drastically change their physical appearance by becoming overweight. A radical change in point of view on body image, as well as a sudden disinterest in how one looks, may signal serious emotional problems. Sometimes, however, as I indicated earlier, this kind of eating may be motivated by an unconscious attempt to break through a wall of resignation and alienation of feelings and to feel alive. In specific answer to the question, however, true thins usually have very little emotional investment in food, and food has very little significance for them in terms of symbolic content. Therefore, they rarely overeat, either in response to appetite surges or in response to emotional upheaval. The overeating response I just described is, it must be understood, very rare. But even those thins who do overeat generally compensate for it long before they experience any appreciable weight gain. In rare cases there are thins who through sustained emotional upheaval "find themselves fat." This can provoke a sense of disorientation and a kind of identity crisis which may produce acute anxiety and depression. People who develop a "shoulds" mentality and make personal contracts about eating little and remaining thin often develop self-hate, guilt, anxiety, and depression if they go against these inner contracts. But this usually happens to fats who are currently thin and hardly ever to true thins. When fats get anxious about regaining weight, they usually do just that—they eat in response to their anxiety and regain the weight they've lost.

Are there true thins who get fat and stay fat?

Well, most people who get and stay fat are fats, not thins at all. But there are rare cases of people who have been thin up into their middle years and who have most of the personality characterics of true thins, who get and stay fat. Essentially, these "special thins," or "fat thins," are often extremely alienated people. Alienation in this context refers to being distanced from one's feelings or having muted or deadened feelings. These people do not function in an integrated way—a way in which all feelings are experienced and lead to a mainstream of consciousness which determines behavior. An alienated person's behavior is a function of repressed and fragmented, compartmentalized aspects of self, each sending out signals to which the individual responds without full conscious awareness, that is without the benefit of an integrated mainstream. In thins who sustain fatness, eating is not hooked (as in the case of true fats or, for our purpose here, "fat fats") to strong appetites of all kinds, but is more of a detached, autonomous habit. These people seldom have other strong appetites (for people, food, sex, sensation, and so on) as do true fats.

Fat and Alive

Then you are really saying that food and eating are extensions of the way fat people feel generally— symbolic of their particular moods at a given time.

Yes, and I take it that we are here referring to an area other than appetite responses to depression and anxiety. Fat people eat when they are happy and are particularly exuberant in their eating practices if they are in a state of mild hypo-mania, or are feeling somewhat "high." Also, as I've indicated in other works, food has high symbolic significance for fat people. This means that the attractiveness of particular foods is dependent upon differing moods. A yearning for sweetness, affection, closeness, and love may lead to a desire for sweet foods. Anger may lead to a desire to "tear into" a solid piece of meat. When they feel convival, fat people like to share food. When they feel down or sullen, they may prefer to eat alone. The manner in which one eats—whether gentle, slow, fast, furious, or shoveling it in to get it over with as quickly as possible— often indicates an extension of feelings generally, though these feelings may be largely repressed and out of the fat person's conscious awareness. Some moods or feelings are never experienced as such, but are completely displaced and dissipated through eating. This is particularly true of very fat, relatively alienated people who may be potentially capable of great exuberance in all areas of life, but experience

61

their vitality only in relation to eating. When the severe food addict begins to get over his food obsessiveness, this exuberance often begins to be experienced in areas other than eating.

I suppose that the digestive processes are, on a purely physiological level, pretty good in fat people. Do you see much indigestion among them?

As a matter of fact I've encountered relatively few digestive problems among the fat. Dyspepsia, gastritis, and more serious digestive disturbances seem to be more common among true thins. I doubt this has anything to do with anatomy or physiology. It may have much more to do with personality and the general effect of emotional factors on the output of digestive juices. Good digestion may also relate to the positive attitude fats have toward food and eating; finding the process pleasurable rather than a tedious necessity may help here. It is also possible that large quantities of food exercise the digestive system and make for more efficient usage, but of course these are all theoretical suppositions. I have interviewed colleagues of mine, who practice internal medicine and surgery, and who agree that gallbladder disease is more common in very fat people but that duodenal ulcers are more common to thin people. (There are exceptions, however.)

Fat and Alive

Inasmuch as convention now approves or even more than approves—even dictates—thinness, are thin people generally happier than fats and are fat people happier when they become thin?

Of course generalizations are subject to both criticism and error, but I'll run those risks. Obviously, since human beings are the most complicated creatures on earth, countless factors beyond weight and society's approbation or condemnation play a role in determining happiness. But all things being equal (and they never are), I believe that fat people have a greater capacity for happiness than thins. This is not because of their fatness, but rather because of the kind of personality they have, the very same qualities that contribute so much to their appetite and fatness in the first place. Of course, society inflicts its prejudices on them, but, despite these, I feel they are still happier than thin people. Fats who become thin and who attempt to change their fat character structures as well as their body size are extremely unhappy. Those who attempt to stay thin, who have no insight into themselves, and who do not accept their "fat personalities" and "fat state of mind" are often miserable. This misery does not usually last long, because the vast majority eat their way back to fatness relatively quickly.

In one of your books you said that fat people are not jolly. Do you still believe this?

I must in this connection point out that for me jolly does not imply superficial bubbly or frothy behavior, nor does it preclude, or in any way dilute, the ability to be utterly sober and serious. For me, jolly alludes to a deep capacity to feel joy, exuberance, and abandon and often includes a capacity to be able to convey this feeling to others.

I believe that fats have a great capacity to be jolly, but that conflict with society's standards, both on a practical reality level as well as on a personal emotional level, often prevents them from exercising this capacity. If they remain fat, they are vilified by the culture they live in. If they become thin, they feel like strangers to themselves. This produces feelings of great constriction and self-hate. It is difficult to be jolly when one is suffering from this kind of inextricable double bind.

Is there a way out?

Yes, but one must be clearly motivated and understand the dynamics involved. Accepting one's "fat personality"—more than accepting it, loving it—while at the same time thinning is the only way out. More than permitting one to sustain thinness, this attitude also makes happiness in all areas of life a

greater possibility, since self-acceptance and compassion for self are crucial to any kind of true self-
realization. The entire second half of this book will,
in fact, deal with the dynamics involved in thinning.

*How come you got thin, and do you accept the fat
man you really are?*

I think I do accept my "fatness," and I continue
the struggle to accept it even more. At times I'm talkative, have large appetites, strong feelings, weep easily, and so on, and I've come to like all these aspects
of myself. I got thin because I have a hiatus hernia,
also known as a diaphragmatic hernia. I had all
kinds of distressing symptoms, and I knew that I'd
either have to get and stay physically thin, or eventually would have to undergo surgery. I preferred thinness, and it has cut down my symptoms a great deal.

*Are you happier thin? Do you see a change in peo-
ple's attitudes toward you?*

People's attitudes toward me have changed. They
no longer joke about my being overweight, nor do I
get gratuitous advice about how to lose weight.
Some people felt threatened when I first lost weight
and told me not to overdo it. Many who recall that I
was fat show me great respect for getting and staying

thin, but some still make hostile remarks, indicating that they expect me to get fat again. I must say this affects me very little, if at all. Thanks to years of psychoanalytic treatment, I'm much more concerned about how *I feel about myself* than what other people think. Being thin has brought no great changes, but I must say I didn't expect it would. I'll talk more about expectations in Part II. All in all I felt more comfortable with myself "fat," and I also still crave the kind of eating I used to do. But, as I just said, I stay thin because of a special health problem, and combating its physical symptoms is important. I suppose there is some vanity in me that is stroked when people say I look good, but I must say that it has no great conscious impact. When people tell me I look younger, this has no impact at all, since I never saw any particular virtue in looking young and am absolutely opposed to a youth-oriented society.

Do you believe there is any special reason that so many poor people are fat?

I think the poor are less involved with and less influenced by cultural niceties. They are largely concerned with survival, and survival is often equated with eating large quantities of food whenever it is available. Many people eat whatever is available in an attempt to store up against hard times. Poor people are often less subject to cultural affectations and retain a spontaneity that involves appetite for feeling, talking, listening, looking, and eating. They are simply not bored, blasé, and deadened. Poor people also eat a great deal of cheap food that is low in nutrients and lacking in protein. They make up for lack of quality by eating in quantity. Their food is often high in starch and calories and low in actual nutritional value. Some poor people, even in these days, still resort to eating commercial starch which may be full of impurities including bacteria. Some formerly poor people retain these eating habits, even after they can afford better food.

Are the various weight groups, Weight Watchers, and so forth, helpful, or hurtful, or both?

I think much depends on the particular group leader or lecturer, as they are sometimes called. If an ambiance of warm support and self-acceptance is promoted within the group, it can be helpful. If fatness is vilified and there is a moral atmosphere of self-righteousness and harsh judgment that promotes self-hate, a group can be harmful. Unfortunately, most of them operate on a symptom-oriented, superficial level. This means that weight loss is all-important, while individual needs, proclivities, and dynamics are neglected. Though some insist that they demand medical, and even psychiatric, "clearance" as a precursor to entry into their programs, I have found that such "clearance" is often perfunctory and phony. The fact is that some people are not ready and may never be ready to lose weight. There are also people to whom weight loss without insight into individual dynamics can be damaging and dangerous to emotional well-being and health.

Do you believe that smoking and alcoholism are addictions related to food addiction?

First, I'd like to distinguish between being fat or heavy, and being a food addict who is malignantly overweight. Degree here is of primary importance. Obviously, being one hundred pounds over insurance charts' normal values is not the same as being ten pounds overweight in a small woman or thirty pounds in a large man. Additionally, and on a psychodynamic level, the addict has, at least to some extent, lost touch with his appetite. He eats compulsively. In his eating, unlike that of his ordinary fat confreres, he eats because of hunger for denied desires and stunted proclivities, rather than as a response to love of food. He eats because he needs to eat to allay anxiety, not because he wants to eat!

I'd like to point out that addicts—real addicts—do have at least some characteristics in common, the main one being, of course, the obsessive use of a particular substance as a means to escape from internal and external conflict. This includes addiction to food, gambling, alcohol, and drugs. They also share neurotic characteristics with the nonaddictive population, though these may be exaggerated in addicts. These often include: great repressed anger, fear of responsibility, poor self-esteem, difficulty in self-assertion, great immaturity, and exaggerated dependency. The question of physiology remains a relatively controversial one, and the experts still don't have hard evidence supporting the role of one's physical chemistry in addiction.

Food addiction, as I've pointed out elsewhere, is particularly difficult to cope with, since food is a necessity of life and therefore cannot be entirely removed from the addict's life. Each contact with food brings on renewed danger inherent in exposure to the addictive substance.

But malignantly overweight people do, from my point of view, differ from other addicts in two regards. First, they are addicted to a substance (food) which is both entirely legal and moral in our society. In other words, the substance of their addiction, unlike other addictions, is completely approved by society. This may indicate that food addicts are far less rebellious than people who use alcohol and drugs. This may be evidence of their greater conformity and passivity than other addicts.

Secondly, very fat people, from my point of view, unlike other addicts, do radically change their body dimensions and how they look. They fall into one of several categories.

A.   Some people are addicted to overeating. These people may even prefer to be thin, but became fat secondary to their compulsion to eat enormous quantities. This group is easier to treat in terms of the goal of becoming regular fats.

B.   This group is addicted to fatness, rather than to overeating. These people eat in order to sustain a state of gross obesity, albeit this motivation usually exists on a totally unconscious level. These are often people who are terrified of any change in their status quo and to whom thinness represents potential change. They, therefore, use the grotesque shape of their bodies to protect themselves against the resolution of inner emotional conflicts, social and sexual conflicts, and self-realization in any of its multiple possibilities—professional, cultural, personal. Many ordinarily fat people fear thinness since it represents lack of substance and feelings of weakness, as well as the threat of new encounters in life—albeit interesting ones. *But* addicts in group B more than fear thinness. For them, thinness produces inordinate terror and is to be shunned at all costs. Because these people are basically very fragile, having extremely poor self-esteem and very little tolerance either for frustration or anxiety, this group is very difficult to treat in terms of thinness as a goal.

C.   This category encompasses people of both the former groups. They are addicted to both the process of eating and to gross obesity. These people are the most difficult to treat and their prognosis is always guarded or uncertain, to say the least.

Is the intestinal bypass surgical operation effective for severe addicts?

It may be effective in terms of reducing weight and sustaining weight loss, but considering its radical nature (eliminating the use and therefore the absorption ability of a large section of intestine), I feel that it is a mutilating procedure and cannot approve of it. By mutilating, I mean modifying and/or destroying normal function. The operation is a major surgical procedure and not without risk and the possibility of complications. It often leaves its subject with chronic diarrhea, plus the possibility of lifelong malnutrition and abnormal underweight. It is too early to ascertain its effect on longevity, but it certainly has secondary effects on one's emotions, in many cases. The fact is that many people who get "psychiatric clearance" before surgery simply go through a perfunctory interview with a psychiatrist that does not evaluate their ability to withstand, unscathed emotionally, this drastic procedure. Of course, the emotional complications only begin with major surgery and continue with post-surgical reactions. The real difficulty involves change in bowel habits and change in body image. However much an individual thinks he or she wants this change, the trauma involved can be devastating. This is because, in many cases, a major defense against anxiety has been precipitously removed, without benefit of psychotherapy, insight, or substitute defenses. Some people respond with depression, and even suicide. Some have attempted to go back to the surgeon to have the procedure reversed. This is not always possible and at best presents the usual surgical hazards. Unfortunately, the best candidates for the procedure, in terms of resistance to emotional complications, are those who don't need it because they can diet successfully. Those who can't diet are the very people who, from an emotional point of view, need their overeating and overweight in order to hold on to a tenuous emotional balance. They are the worst candidates. There are even a number of people who have undergone surgery who have never been really fat at all. Some have been regular fats who have been unduly influenced by hostile surroundings. Some have even been very alienated thins who are obsessed with being still thinner and terrified of overweight. The sad truth is that people who want surgery badly enough will eventually find a "doctor" who will do it, even if it is bad for them. In many cases, this operation which, at best, deals with a problem on the most superficial basis also produces the equivalent of a chronic colitis in what was originally (before surgery) a normal bowel.

Of the addicts, which category is more likely to be a better candidate, that is, which would have fewer complications following bypass surgery?

I think complications are inevitable, even if they are relatively mild ones. I also feel that each person must be evaluated individually, regardless of category. But from a theoretical point of view (theoretical because I cannot approve in any case), all things being equal, Group A—people addicted to eating only and not to fatness—would do better. People who are addicted to being grossly overweight may, in finding themselves suddenly and precipitously losing weight, go into a terrible panic. This panic can produce a psychotic reaction when these people find themselves irreversibly thin and trapped in a body which is totally unfamiliar and disorienting. If adaptation is impossible, chronic depression, lasting for an entire lifetime, may ensue. If it is, for whatever compelling reason, impossible to withhold surgery, I feel that psychoanalytic treatment is indicated for at least a year before surgery and for an extended period of time following the operation. Hopefully, the effects of the preoperative analytic therapy would convince the person not to undertake this drastic procedure at all.

Is there any effective treatment or regimen of some kind that can be used effectively for severe addicts?

Ideally, treatment involves a multiple approach. Initial hospitalization is probably indicated in order to establish a good beginning. But even this can only be effective in a proper therapeutic milieu, which would include a thorough physical, as well as psychological, work-up and investigation. In the hospital, care would be taken to augment the person's total health as well as establish an appropriate diet. Psychotherapy is of course absolutely indicated, and a group psychotherapeutic experience would probably be helpful. After a proper evaluation is done and a proper hospital-supervised diet is initiated, psychotherapy to get at underlying problems would be the main thrust. But, I would add, the supportive adjunct of a buddy system like the one found in Overeaters Anonymous (as in AA or GA—Gamblers Anonymous) would be extremely desirable. The kind of twenty-four-hour support that OA provides may be critical, especially in the early stages of serious dieting. The need to communicate with a supportive person at any time of the day or night to help prevent a catastrophic binge is not uncommon in severe addicts. The members of Overeaters Anonymous cooperate with each other on this basis, since their empathy is based on personal experience. But, from my point of view, understanding the psychodynamics involved on a personal and gut level is

74

still necessary, especially if the person is to sustain weight loss once it has taken place. This is true of the fat non-addict and is a thousand times more true of the addict. Personal and gut means that which goes beyond general and intellectual understanding. One must relive and feel much that has gone on and continues to go on in one's life especially when it comes to conditions that produce anxiety and set up connections between anxiety and food and fatness.

Understanding the symbols involved and the image one has of oneself is crucial. The most effective method for achieving this understanding is still psychoanalytic psychotherapy. Severe addicts must be in psychoanalysis for a long period of time, and in some cases all their lives. They suffer from an incurable, chronic illness, but one which *is* controllable. However, healthy control requires a great deal of expert attention. Of course, this also includes medical attention. Enormous loss of weight—in some cases as much as four-fifths of one's body substance—requires very careful medical supervision.

Do you believe in starvation, or near-starvation, diets just to get started in weight reduction, especially for severe addicts?

Starvation diets are easier than controlled diets for very fat people. Melodramatic gestures, all-or-nothing approaches, and any kind of magical intervention are attractive to people who are exuberant by nature. But they are easier for another reason, too. Where the addiction is to food, obviously any contact with the addicting substance, food, will produce a craving for more. Total abstinence removes this craving. But food is ultimately necessary! The process of eating is requisite to living. As I pointed out, in this regard, food addiction is different from addiction to alcohol, tobacco, or heroin, which the body can very well do without. Starvation and gimmick diets are not realistic for the long run and are the antithesis of what is needed for a healthier lifelong orientation to food and eating. They can also be dangerous for short periods of time. This is especially true for people who have any kind of metabolic disturbance: hypoglycemia, diabetes, potassium deficiency, and so on. Sometimes starvation, or very low-calorie, high-protein, diets are indicated for a short period of time in cases where the patient suffers great respiratory difficulty or heart failure, but obviously, strict medical supervision is indicated in these cases. I feel that radical approaches to diet, when applied to the general population, are ultimately destructive both physically and emotionally as well as from the point of view of weight control. When they are used prudently, hospitalization as well as strict medical supervision is almost always necessary.

Fat and Alive

Do you believe in the fat cell theory—that is, that children who are overfed develop more fat cells which preclude their being anything but fat for the rest of their lives?

I know very little about it, though I've heard the pros and cons about "fat cells." I believe that very little fatness is organic, that is, physical in nature. Endocrine imbalance does occur but is relatively rare. Ordinary fatness, or heaviness, is, I feel, largely an extension of a particular character structure and is neither inherited nor acquired through any kind of metabolic interference as a child. While some aspects of character structure may be inherited, a large part of our personality development is influenced by how we relate to various members of our immediate families as young children. The kinds of personalities we develop will largely determine the kinds of appetites we have. Grossly fat people and severely thin people—addicts and people we may call food phobics—also respond largely to personality characteristics. In these extreme cases, severe personality problems are invariably present and manifest themselves in the way addicts and phobics relate to themselves, to other people, and to food as well.

May I point out here that some very fat people form "eating bonds" with other fat people. This means that they use food and eating as their main activity in relating to each other. Some have learned to

77

"bond" in this way from early childhood, and go on to do so with husbands, wives, children, and friends for the rest of their lives. In these cases redirection of relating activity—that is, finding other areas of mutual interest—is crucial if weight loss is to be sustained.

Well, in sum, what are ordinary fat people or heavy people like?

There are exceptions, and of course each person is an individual, but much of the following applies to fat people. I should point out that on occasion some of these characteristics are repressed or masked. Fatness itself in our society sometimes makes it difficult for the person in question to behave as he or she really feels. Addicts do not fall into this category. While they may have some of these characteristics, they often *do not*. Again, it is important not to confuse ordinary heavy people with grossly obese people. Many of the super fat have severe emotional problems and often have more in common with extreme thins than with anyone else. In fact, both severe thins and the severely overweight are often relatively asexual, lacking in real appetites (for food, sex, and so on). Even though they eat compulsively, they lack zest and may be relatively reserved or even withdrawn.

Ordinarily heavy people are often very alive, vital,

sensuous people. They are tuned in to their senses and have keen, large appetites in all areas of life. They like to feel, touch, smell, taste, see and swallow. Sex plays a large part in their lives, as does eating, talking, and exchanging feelings and ideas with others. These strong feelings and appetites are often expressed with exuberance and abandon. Fat people are especially exuberant about eating, and often without conscious awareness feel their abandon most through eating. Indeed, they may, through self-effacement and self-hate, repress their other appetites, and they may also be unaware that they channel their sense of letting go and complete abandon into eating.

I have told some repressed fat people about this sense of abandon experienced through eating and rarely through any other area, and it has often been a great revelation to them. Eating with gusto and complete abandon is one of the most important characteristics of fat people and must be understood in any successful thinning program which is undertaken. Fat people are "people people" and can both receive and give from and to other people. They are naturally gregarious and generally prefer being in company to being alone. If they have not been embarrassed by too much criticism and humiliation regarding weight, they tend to be somewhat exhibitionistic, loving to take center stage and receive admiration.

They are surprisingly active people, and if they are comfortable with others, often enjoy dancing, which a great many of them do with great grace. But they don't always dance.

They are moody people given to highs and lows and relatively few "even periods." They have a need to be liked and are often devastated if they are rejected. Therefore, they are often dependent on other people and on other people's good will, a dependence that makes them very vulnerable. They also have poor frustration tolerance, poor anxiety tolerance, and a high susceptibility to depression.

To summarize—let me list the qualities that are more often than not appropriate to them and easily apparent in encountering them: Exuberance, appetite, abandon, zest, sensuality, sensitivity, expressiveness, enthusiasm, jocosity, vitality, sadness, aliveness, strong feeling, social experience, involvment, responsiveness.

In short they contain, represent, and express much of the stuff of humanity, sometimes in such abundance as to be overwhelming.

TWO

Thinning

Thinning is the process of getting thin and staying thin. Very few fat people are successful in this process. Many get thin but few stay that way. The two phases of this process must be viewed as a well-integrated whole. This means that even as the individual begins to lose weight, he or she must at the same time be engaged in the process of sustaining the weight loss. In other words—sustaining weight loss does not begin after the desired weight loss has taken place. If this is attempted, which it usually is, failure results and the weight is regained with a vengeance. Sustaining weight loss must begin even before any weight is lost; that is, before serious dieting begins.

The process must continue then as dieting and

loss of weight takes place and it must go on after weight loss is complete. The entire process is largely a psychological one requiring insight into thinning as well as into individual personal characteristics. Without insight, success is just about impossible. Remember that in dealing with fatness and thinness we are principally dealing with character structure or personality and with our emotional lives. Fatness, thinness, and pathological states involving exaggerations of one or the other states are extensions of our emotional selves—how we view ourselves, others, and the world. Neglecting this aspect of dieting makes successful thinning impossible, and it is the reason so many people fail as they seek out various magic diet solutions without considering their psychological outlooks.

I will speak about diet briefly, but specific diets are seldom the problem. Nearly all diets result in weight loss, and there are few doctors who know more about dieting to lose weight than fat people. But no diet works, no drugs work—*nothing* works— unless the central issue is tackled. The central issue in thinning is psychological insight. I've provided some insight in my earlier books *The Thin Book by a Formerly Fat Psychiatrist* and *Forever Thin*. In the following pages I describe fifteen insights which I've since come to consider vital to success in thinning.

1.

Motivation

Why do you want to be thinner? The answer to this question is crucial and knowing it is absolutely a must before beginning this difficult endeavor. The answer must be an open, honest one. This does not mean that any of us are conscious liars in answering this or other questions about ourselves. Most of us have simply not gotten used to self-revelatory investigation and have settled for answering in superficial clichés. "It's better to be thin." "I just want to knock off some weight." "I think it will make me feel better," and so on. These answers neither promote nor sustain the kind of motivation necessary for continued success in thinning.

We must be clear and precise about what it is that motivates us.

Is it a health issue, and if so, is this an imaginary health issue or a real one? Is there one factor involved or more than one? Some people are prone to diabetes or high blood pressure or hypoglycemic attacks. Others have heart conditions or need surgery which would be aided by a thin abdomen. Some have a gallbladder condition or other digestive disturbances. Has there been adequate discussion with a physician? Adequate in this connection means one which you come away from having taken nothing for granted and absolutely not having settled for just a simple statement from your doctor like, "I want you to lose weight," however well-intended. *Adequate* means that you come away thoroughly understanding why being thinner than you are is important to your health. You do not have to be a doctor to understand an explanation of what and how weight affects the particular condition or physical problem you have. You must come away understanding these connections thoroughly enough to be convinced that sustained weight loss will improve your health and help you to sustain a healthier and longer life. Remember please, this understanding must not be based on your doctor's blanket statement, but rather on your complete comprehension of his detailed explanation. Ask him the necessary questions. Press for full and clear replies. If he refuses to answer, then it is time to change doctors. When I first became interested in treating fat people, I was amazed at the answers I got when I asked my patients why they wanted to be thin. Some were very vague. Most hardly knew their motivations at all, and just about none were specific. I soon realized that I had to ask more specific and detailed questions in order to help them get started and to clarify and develop particular motivations.

Do you want to get thinner for business reasons? Are you an actor? Model? Dancer? Salesperson? Do you feel that thinness will bring more respect and recognition in the work you do? Are your business colleagues particularly prejudiced against heavy people? Does appearance and cultural acceptance of a thin image play an important role in your professional and economic life? How about your social life? Are you tired of being limited in the choice of clothes you can wear?

Is your desire to lose weight largely a question of social acceptance, personal vanity, and the need to conform? Does actual embarrassment play a role? I remember a woman I saw in consultation whose main motivation was the fact that her husband and children were embarrassed by her weight. She was heavy but not grotesque. It is important not to dislike yourself if vanity and the need for conformity are your principal motivating forces. If these are, in fact, making you miserable, you are better off knowing about them, accepting them, and using them as motivating forces rather than lying to yourself, repressing awareness of your feelings, and continuing to hate yourself for having them.

Are you tired of being discriminated against in all areas of your life? Do you find you cannot put down your oversensitivity to what people will think of you? Do you feel that you must be thinner in order to effect a change in some important aspect of your life? I saw a woman recently whose marriage has been disastrous for years. She felt she could never dissolve her marriage unless she became thin, since her heavy status precluded the possibility of a social life as a single woman. In our society her reasoning unfortunately has considerable practical basis and it is good that she is clear about her motive.

Motivation sometimes comes from a combination of these things, and at times, from still other sources. Examine your own motivations carefully and review them periodically. This review is important both during dieting and during maintenance of thinness once weight is lost. It is not a bad idea to write out the various reasons for losing weight and to read over the list every several weeks, or whenever you are on the brink of a potential eating binge.

2.

The Paradox

Simply stated, the paradox is that we must accept ourselves as we are, if we want to change ourselves constructively and permanently. If we accept ourselves as we are, why then, you ask, would we want to change? The answer is that human beings can grow and change in a *healthy* direction, whatever their condition, and however old they are. *But* change that takes place motivated by self-hate (or hatred for how we are before we change) is not healthy or constructive change and does not lead to sustained growth in a healthy direction. If an individual wants to get thin because he hates himself heavy, his getting thin will be part of a self-idealizing, perfectionistic, compulsive process that will lead to ever increasing self-hate, and eventually, back to fatness and perhaps even to malignant fatness and even more self-hate.

If self-acceptance is absent, effort to ostensibly aid oneself will be futile, because what happens is as follows. Dieting on a conscious level is perceived by the dieter as an effort or even a constructive struggle to improve himself, but on an unconscious level, it is felt as an attack on his own natural proclivities (healthy appetite, vitality, and so on) and as a process of self-diminution and destruction. Thus, without conscious awareness, the dieter is thrown into an anxiety-producing conflict of major proportions, in which both dieting and eating lead to self-hate. The dieter tries to diet, but this makes him anxious, because on an unconscious level, he is going against himself. If he breaks the diet and eats, he becomes anxious because he is going against a conscious contract he made with himself to diet. The key to the problem is the contract and real self-acceptance.

There is a major and crucial difference between a *contract* made with oneself to lose weight and a *free choice decision*. The contract is born of tyranny, and if broken, leads to self-hate, depression, and renewed eating. Its purpose is self-glorification and perfectionism. A free decision to diet is born of a desire for change, but the dieter's goals are usually realistic and within human limitations. Breaking the diet, in this case, does not lead to anxiety and more eating, but to sympathy with oneself and a renewed attempt to diet.

90

In dealing with a contract, the scale becomes the externalized policeman and tells us whether or not we dare to feel good. In dealing with a self-accepting decision, the scale remains a scale, is not used excessively, does not determine our moods, and is only an aid to indicate the effect of dieting. In short, it is not used as a criterion for living up to the contract—or for feeling like a "good" or "bad" girl or boy. Self-acceptance predicated on weight loss is not self-acceptance at all. Self-acceptance only exists where there is no blackmail whatsoever. Self-acceptance can only take place in weight reduction, if the individual stands up against cultural pressures, prejudices, and dicta to be thin. This means that he must like himself despite other people's disapproval or dislike, and even though he wants to change and get thin! Peculiarly and paradoxically, we must stand up against the culture to successfully get along in and with the culture. Understanding and working through this paradox is of prime importance in sustaining weight loss. This is so, because it is hard enough to lose weight for someone else through self-hate, but it is almost impossible to sustain the loss, unless it is done for yourself through love of the self.

3.

Retaining Fat Personality

Thinning involves more than standing up to the culture and taking a stand against making contracts. Thinning also involves knowing, liking, and retaining those aspects of personality characteristic of and linked to "being fat," even as the attempt is made to become and to stay physically thin. In other words, we must love and help our fat "souls," as we become thin bodies.

Thus, we must make an attempt to know on a deep level, that is to feel, the intensity of our appetites, yearnings, sensuality, vitality, love of people, love of talking, our mood swings, outgoingness and lack of reserve. We must like these and all aspects of ourselves. Indeed, we must *love* them, and we must make every effort against any attempt to transform ourselves into a kind of culturally-approved stereo-type. We must give up any attempt to become strong, silent, withdrawn, reserved, spare, sparse human be-ings—we must work harder to accept who we are and to reject attempts at self-idealization. This reten-tion of "self" mitigates against the feeling of loss of identity as body dimensions change. Thus, the per-son continues to feel like him or herself, however much "physical substance" is lost, because "psy-chological substance" remains intact. This is an an-tidote to anxiety and depression, both of which drive the individual back to eating, because overeating is always a habitual defense response to anxiety and mild depression in fat people and is also an attempt to regain a sense of identity and solidity.

But retention of the "fat personality" is important beyond the role this plays in successful thinning. It is also important in living a compassionate and con-structive life with one's self and onefellows. We may for whatever reason decide to lose weight, but this is no reason to amputate and to gouge out some of our most human and constructive personality aspects. In *Forever Thin* I described the Fear of Thinness as an important insight into the reason for remaining fat. My view in this regard has not changed. It is impor-tant that we include fear of thinness in this insight into retaining a fat personality. Simply stated, fat people, and especially very fat people, unconscious-ly fear thinness, even as they desire to get thin. This is so because thinness unconsciously represents having to face the possibility of struggling to fulfill all kinds of standards and expectations which up to that point were rationalized away as impossibilities since the person was simply "too fat to do anything." Thinness represents a change in the status quo and a potential confrontation with "a whole new way of life." Unfamiliarity, plus the possibility of disappointment and failure to achieve what is expected of a newly-thin person creates enough anxiety to give a fat person a phobia when it comes to achieving and sustaining a state of thinness.

But it is more than that, too, and I want to add it here. Thinness also represents a kind of psychological lobotomy. In the unconscious mind of the fat person, thinness is equated with giving up aliveness, exuberance, vitality, gusto and abandon—thus, while it is very attractive on the cultural level, it is felt as extremely threatening in personal terms. Therefore, it is necessary to dissociate the state of fatness from the fat personality. The fat person must come to realize that he or she can give up being fat in body, while "fatness of feelings," largeness of spirit is retained. Thinness must likewise be dissociated from "fatness of feelings or personality." One can become and stay thin while retaining all the psychological characteristics of being fat. But expectations of what thinness will bring to life must be reduced to realistic proportions so that advance fear of disappointment is removed! I shall have more to say about this a little later on.

4.

Feeling the Conflict

Weight groups, therapists, diet books, and friends tell you about the joys, marvels, and benefits of being thin. Nobody mentions the joy of eating with abandon and sustaining fatness. It is a mistake for fat people who want to be thin to attempt to repress or to rationalize away this joy. Doing so leaves a sense of emptiness and yearning to which they eventually succumb. The desire to *eat,* if repressed, retains its strength, takes on autonomy, and is eventually heard from in hurricane strength, usually leading straight to a "super binge." Repressing the truth, especially strong feelings and appetites, does not work! Forces which are pushed into unconscious awareness exert more influence than those we are fully conscious of because we cannot exert conscious choice and control over them. They operate from their own autonomous position out of the mainstream, split off from the center of consciousness, and undiluted by conscious rationale.

It is, therefore, imperative that before undertaking a serious thinning endeavor, a conscious decision be made regarding that choice. This can only be meaningful if the individual experiences the conflict between the desire to go on eating freely versus the desire to thin on a fully conscious level! It is not enough to list, to describe, and to feel out the virtues of being thin. You must also with full awareness and open feelings experience the joys of *free eating.*

Some fat patients I have had in treatment initially felt that I was strange, and even destructive, because I wanted them to talk about the joy of eating freely and voluminously. One woman I saw a few years ago admitted that she several times thought of quitting treatment with me because she was nearly convinced that I was trying to get her to eat more. But she stayed on and came to understand that I was trying to get her to experience her real feelings, all of them, including those which made for uncomfortable conflict. This is the only way to make real decisions, especially about something as tough as thinning.

Yes, you must know what is being given up, and of course something must be given up, which is always the case when a real decision—rather than a perfunctory, compliant, conforming, compulsive one is made. This involves feeling out the loss felt in giving up free eating—the sensual taste of the food, the free eating of unlimited quantity, the sense of fullness, and so on. Feeling out both sides of the conflict involves considerable struggle. This is not pleasant, but it leads to full conscious awareness of the choice, the decision, and ultimately the will to act on a responsible adult level which is necessary to sustain success.

5.

Abandon or Letting Go

Very few fat people are aware that eating is usually one of the very few activities, and sometimes the only, activity that provides them almost a complete sense of abandon or letting go. Some fat people experience this sense of abandon on the dance floor. Others feel it in sex, but many, an enormous number, feel it through eating. Abandon is extremely important to exuberant, vital people. It is an outlet for abundant energy and, as such, acts as a kind of safety valve for subsequent relaxation. It is also a form of self-expression and a great source of self-realization. The total effect of letting go or abandon or total investment of self (even for a few moments at a time)—a becoming one with whatever activity one is

101

participating in—is an enriching, life-affirming experience.

That fat people often experience this feeling in eating, and sometimes only in eating, makes this kind of abandon in eating very difficult to surrender, if not, in some cases, impossible. Indeed, I believe that in many cases the great pull to huge eating binges is actually a desire for abandon. But very few people are consciously aware that eating serves the purpose of letting go. Even as it happens, the dynamic or motivation involved, as well as the satisfaction derived, is repressed to an unconscious level. It is very important that the person in question put him or herself in complete touch with the feeling, otherwise the *conflict* will not really be resolved, and the yearning for food, which actually represents a yearning for a sense of freedom or letting go, will continue. This eventually leads to an urge to rebel against a diet contract (rather than a real choice and decision) and a monumental binge, followed by a return to old eating habits.

With the kind of exuberance fat people possess, the need for abandon does not fade away nor does it have to be obliterated. Though it may seem impossible, it can be transferred to other areas of living with nearly equal, if not completely equal, satisfaction. Abandon can be applied to work, at least some of the time. You can also turn the urge to let go to game playing, love—both feeling love and making love—and to other interests such as art, music, socializing, talking, dancing, and exercising. I've written elsewhere, and I still believe, that exercise plays a very small role in weight reduction. Dieting is the thing! Exercise is valuable in giving a person a sense of his or her body. But I want also to state that exercise can offer an area for abandon. In exercising, you can let go. This is as true of any calisthenic kind of exercising as it is of walking, running, swimming or playing games: tennis, handball, squash, and so on. Of course, any physical activity must be preceded by a proper medical consultation and must be appropriate to one's physical condition.

Some years ago I had a fat patient in treatment who was a writer. After considerable struggle and much insight, he simultaneously dieted while he transferred his feelings of abandon from eating to writing. His writing became freer, more creative, and far more effective generally. This made controlled eating easier and led to a sense of well-being, which further improved his writing, establishing a constructive cycle. Interestingly, before he left treatment, he began to paint, too, something he previously only thought about, but could not "let go and do." I feel that this was possible only because he got in touch with his need and feel for abandon while transferring it from eating to other arenas of his life.

I cannot stress enough the importance of retaining this sense of abandon in at least one (or more) areas. It is vital to successful thinning, and it is also enormously helpful in sustaining good moods, a healthy outlook, and in some measure, preventing depression and anxiety.

6.

Connections

Fat people are very reactive people and feel all kinds of emotions strongly. This does not exclude anger. Most people in our culture have difficulty with feeling and expressing anger. I detailed the difficulties involved in *The Angry Book*. But fat people in their overwhelming desire to be liked and admired, or at least tolerated, despite their fatness, have particular difficulty with anger. This is especially true of grossly obese people. Indeed, I believe that a large part of their obesity is due to an inability to handle angry feelings and express them through regular channels. Instead of "letting go" with anger, they often "take it out" on food and eating.

Repressed anger leads to anger at oneself and directly to depression. In an attempt to ward off depression, fat people will eat in order to counter sadness with pleasure; to add to themselves a sense of substantiality and strength; to feel love and warmth symbolized by foods and memories of maternal care expressed through feeding; and also, to "attack food" in an active way that allows the discharge of anger or angry energy. Thus, eating binges are often depression equivalents or, more accurately, defenses against depression, as well as serving as actual avenues of anger discharge. By means of the binge, the fat person either avoids depression or goes on to be depressed anyway. If depression occurs and is strong, it usually terminates the binge. When depression is over, appetite returns.

Anxiety usually occurs when anger is about to surface despite attempts to repress it. Anxiety can also lead to eating attacks. Being aware of these connections can be very valuable. The fat person must come to realize that an overwhelming urge to go on a binge may indeed be evidence of repressed anger signaling impending anxiety and depression. Making these "connections" by examining one's feelings and permitting oneself to feel, and even to express, anger may prevent the binge and the anxiety and depression as well. It can also, eventually, lead to a healthier attitude toward anger. The knowledge that being universally liked is impossible, of no value, and far too costly, both emotionally and physically, can be liberating.

When fat people stop eating they must expect to

106

feel anger. If they want to continue dieting on a relatively successful level, that is with binges limited in duration and frequency, they must permit themselves to feel, and even to express, their anger. If this is done as soon as it is felt, anger will probably never get beyond the level of mild irritation. Anger which is avoided, either unconsciously (repression) or consciously (suppression), snowballs into massive outbursts. Dieting brings on actual discharge of anger for two principal reasons: 1. Heavy eating provides both an outlet for anger and a symbolic means of pushing down anger with food. When this is given up, the stored up anger is released. 2. Denying appetites that are accustomed to immediate gratification engenders feelings of frustration that bring on anger, if not full-blown rage. This is readily understood when we realize that fat people have a poor frustration tolerance that corresponds to their more vivid experience of anxiety. Unlike their true thin confreres, they are not good at waiting, curtailing, or limiting themselves, especially in areas where they have strong appetites. They want what they want *now*, and the need to wait makes for anger. This anger must be dealt with on an increasingly open and honest basis to counteract the impulse to go on a destructive binge in either stage one (losing weight) or stage two (sustaining weight loss) of thinning.

I had a very fat lady in treatment who saw herself as all-loving, gentle, sweet and "never angry." For some time she successfully resisted any attempt I made to acquaint her with the possibility that she did in fact repress considerable anger. Interestingly, I managed to reveal that most of her eating binges took place directly after a verbal attack by her husband, who was frequently very vindictive. But, she could not, or would not, make the connection. She was a very self-effacing and compliant woman, and the idea of anger, let alone rage, at her husband was too threatening to the image she had established in herself of goodness capable of surmounting even angry feelings. For several months she lost no weight in treatment. Her husband continued his tirades and she continued to eat. I then thought of working things through backwards from the symptom to the source in an effort to break this deadlock. I managed to get her to agree to eat whenever she wanted to *except following her husband's tirades.* She managed to do it—to not eat when he got vindictive with her. She experienced her anger! More than that, she became enraged and let him have it—years and years of stored up vitriol.

This was followed by considerable anxiety because her picture of herself as always being "nice" and placid was given a sharp jolt. But she quickly got used to her new, quite human, and honest status. The rewards that followed were considerable. 1. She was able to control her eating and lost over one hundred pounds. 2. She became a far more self-assertive person and, as she cast off her neurotic angelic mantle, she became a much more real and more interest-

nb, nb 9nb,

Thinning

ing person. 3. Not feeling the helplessness she did when she was non-assertive reduced her anger enormously. At the same time, when she did get angry she was able to express it rather than having to repress and store it in the experience of eating. 4. Her relationship with her husband improved. All of this did not happen overnight. It took much time and considerable struggle, but the breakthrough occurred as I have described it.

109

7.

Standards

By standards, I simply mean the amount of weight you want to lose, the weight you wish to attain and live with, and the length of time or rate of loss you have in mind. You might also include the range of gain and loss permitted after you have attained your goal.

Fat people do just about everything in a big way. It is no surprise then that they set themselves goals which are impossible to fulfill. Interestingly, and unfortunately, this is one of the few areas in which fats become quite rigid and uncompromising. They too often "decide" to lose weight more rapidly than is either feasible or possible to sustain. They also allow little or no leeway for fluctuation once a goal is achieved.

I cannot stress enough the importance of this "insight." Standards must be constructed which are realistic, otherwise the weight loss is inevitably doomed. Indeed, this is one of the principal causes of lifelong weight fluctuation, resulting in the loss and gain of literally thousands of pounds in a single lifetime. I shall have more to say about rate of loss in the insight on dieting, but it is important to say here and now that attempts to establish and sustain an impossible weight loss rate will inevitably lead to disaster. I mean this quite clearly in terms of destruction 1. to weight reduction regimens, 2. to emotional health, and 3. to physical health. Severe dietary restrictions, starvation or gimmick diets, and drug aids are fraught with disaster, especially when they become for a dieter a chronic and constant lifestyle.

It is not wise to embark on thinning with no weight standards in mind. Fat people do not do well if they don't have clearly delineated standards in mind. Vague expectations of weight loss lead to a haphazard approach to diet, and eventually to chaos, impulsive eating, and the end of dieting. So it is of great importance that the person involved know that he or she must establish standards—that is, a clear concept of rate of loss and weight to be attained. It is important to remember that initial weight loss is usually greater (because of water loss) and almost always slows appreciably as time goes on. Expectations of a dramatic weight loss beginning at once

112

and continuing right to the desired weight will lead to severe disappointment, and inevitable eating. Even if rapid loss *is* achieved, it will not be maintained. I'll say more about this in my discussion on dieting. An initial attempt to lose two pounds a week and eventually accommodate the loss of half a pound or a pound a week may sound paltry, but it is realistic. Of course these standards may be scaled up or down to fit individual cases of very large people or extremely small people.

Interestingly, many of us fats apply our appetite for food to our appetite for weight loss: once we decide to lose, we tend to consider the loss of a pound a week virtually no loss at all. After all, we are used to viewing ourselves and everything else—weight loss included—in a big way. *But* those single pounds add up, and this appropriate (not slow, only slow compared to the instant gratification we learned to expect from food and now transfer to thinness) rate of loss makes it easier to sustain the loss later on.

Now about the goal. We cannot and must not in our zeal establish a goal that makes no sense in terms of our past history, personality and body type. A metamorphosis will not take place, and if it could, it would not be desirable. We cannot shrink bones and we must not shrink muscle tissue! We are what we are, and for the most part, we ought largely to go on being who we are. Many of us are large people.

In any case, before we start out, it is vital to observe ourselves realistically and evaluate where we've been, where we are, and where we intend to go. If this journey is senseless in terms of our personal reality, it will, at best, remain only a dream, and at worst, turn into nightmare. Remember, there is no "cure" for ordinarily heavy people because there is no "sickness." Getting too thin is as much a sickness as getting too fat. But as I've said elsewhere, even where fatness is a sickness because of its grossness, this food addiction is not curable; it is only controllable.

Anyway, the goal must not be to transform a large person into a small one, a big-boned person into a frail, wispy person. The best standard is a realistic one. Getting rid of flab is okay and so is reducing a pot belly, but attempting *Vogue* model proportions is foolhardy. It is also foolhardy to expect a big appetite for food to go away because you now have a big appetite for thinness. Standards for weight loss must be realistic and commensurate with food needs. Also, once you achieve a realistic weight, you cannot expect your weight to stay at exactly that point. You must allow yourself some leeway. A fluctuation of three to five pounds in either direction is usual. Overly stringent standards will lead either to no loss of weight, or to regaining what has been lost, or to adding still more weight. Reality measured in terms of a deliberate rate of goal-directed loss will help a dieter retain a healthy body and spirit commensurate with his history, personality, and body type, even while he sheds some excess poundage.

114

Do not be goaded by ridiculous cultural standards into developing equally foolish standards for yourself. Choosing a standard which is comfortable for you is the best guarantee of success. Comfortable means realistically comfortable with yourself, physically and emotionally.

8.

Expectations

Thin people do not have more fun, and you will not have more fun when you get thinner either! This is not a cruel statement. It is an insight *vital* to the process of thinning, and it is a compassionate one. Expectations of a Shangri-la—heavenlike existence brought on by thinness—are certain to bring disappointment, bitterness, and an onslaught of cynicism which inevitably lead to a return of weight. Also, the knowledge that thinness brings thinness and little else (of course, it may, in line with your original motivations, help a gallbladder condition, make you less directly the target of cruel remarks by other people, and so on, but these are not heaven-on-earth expectations) is an excellent antidote to the fear of thinness and thus aids the thinning process.

The fat person brings himself to thinness with assets and problems intact, much as a person brings him or herself to a marriage or to a new place to live. Marriage and new places resolve very few problems, and the same is true of thinness. Actually, all three pose problems because adjustments are necessary whenever we encounter an unfamiliar situation. However, thinness can in an indirect way help in resolving problems, because if eating freely and excessively acts as a defense against anxiety and as an aid in repressing unwanted feelings, removal of that defense may make problems more accessible and therefore easier to resolve, albeit more painful.

The worst part of exorbitant expectations is that they are actually demands on ourselves for a more perfect way of life. Thus, the process of thinning is equated (mostly unconsciously) with a need for more perfect performance—at work, in sex, at play and on the social scene. This kind of demand or expectation of self represents a form of self-exploitation and self-hate, and ultimately has a sufficiently demoralizing effect, to cause a dieter to view weight loss with keen apprehension.

I might point out that there is often a direct relationship between expectations of "perfect dieting" (no slips from the diet at all!), expected weight loss, and general expectations involving a more perfect life. This means that the individual who expects the most physical change (and usually enormously exaggerated physical change) also expects change to take

118

place without a hitch and anticipates the most ideal-
ized existence once this change takes place. It therefore behooves the "perfectionistic dieter," who is
striving for thinness beyond realistic standards, to
be especially careful of exorbitant expectations in all
areas of living once his desired weight is reached.

9.

The Diet

Most fat people know more about weight reduction diets than anyone else, including the experts. But this does not mean that they know about nourishment, how to select diets appropriate to physical condition, or have a realistic and practical outlook concerning diets that can work. Their knowledge of diets is often clouded and even grossly distorted by impatience and a desire to lose weight the "easy way." Thus, victimization of the fat by pill-pushers, gimmick diet charlatans, faddists, and all kinds of ignorant and ruthless practitioners abounds. This is so, despite the fact that most fat people know deep down that there is no magic to weight loss and that drugs and fad diets score temporarily, but are inevitably followed by abject failure, and sometimes, even physical and emotional collapse.

To ask fat people to slow down and to take it easy in dieting is to ask them to engage in a most difficult but worthwhile struggle. Fat people are not good at postponing rewards when both their desire and the energy necessary to fulfill that desire is experienced now. Yet, this is precisely what must be done, because only a *slow* diet will ultimately work.

Doctors can perform a very important service by checking out physical health and designing a diet appropriate to individual need. Here again, it is important that the patient understand the doctor's rationale, even though some of the nutritional detail may require a bit of serious study to comprehend. The effort is surely worth it, because the dieter can then become a completely active participant in his diet, rather than a passive subject. By taking the time to understand the kind of diet given, what foods are allowed on it, and how they work, the dieter can make innovative changes if necessary or desired without spoiling the diet and without being so dependent on his doctor that he has to run to him for approval of every alteration in the plan.

Strange as it may seem, many fat people are undernourished, especially during times of dieting. They may lack necessary vitamins as well as potassium, iron, and other nutritional elements. This can be disastrous to both health and dieting. Tissues require all kinds of nutrients, especially during weight loss to ward off illness and to allow for proper repair and growth. But "undernourishment" (regardless of how much weight gain or loss takes place) leads straight to fatigue. As I've described elsewhere, fatigue in fat people leads to eating—usually indiscriminate eating. Often this is accompanied by an overwhelming craving for sugar. This usually signals the beginning of the end of dieting. The two great enemies of diet effort are fatigue and hunger, and in fat people, they are usually seen in unison, or close on each other's heels. Therefore it is important that any diet have: 1. All the necessary nutrients to prevent food deprivation fatigue and hunger, and 2. Enough bulk so that the dieter doesn't suffer from psychological food hunger in which he feels that he isn't eating enough. Obviously, in this last connection, low-calorie foods of all kinds are extremely valuable.

Making sure with a doctor of appropriateness and proper nutrition on an individual basis, the diet I favor most is one which is *mixed* and *slow*. The mixed, calorie-controlled kind of diet not only contains the nutrients necessary for health and vitality (anti-fatigue), but also has the advantage of being the least boring and most supportable over the long run. This kind of diet may be difficult at first because of the lack of dramatic early results, but it pays off over the long haul. Gimmick diets—for example, all protein—not only have a full potential for physical damage, but also become boring and dull eventually, and make for great craving for normal food. This usually leads to a binge, in which the dieter wipes out all "gains" made up to that point. Even more important—the gimmick diet does not lend itself to easy conversion to normal eating patterns during phase two of thinning—the difficult, all-important phase of keeping weight off for the rest of one's life. It is simply not possible or practical to live a long life on a starvation diet, whether that be an all-protein diet, an ice cream diet, or any of the other fad schemes.

The closer one's weight reduction diet is to a regular maintenance diet, the easier it will be to adjust physically and psychologically to maintenance simply by adding quantities of food and calories to what one has been eating for some time. In a "normal," low-calorie, mixed diet, the dieter, all through the phase one weight reduction period, is in effect already adjusting and preparing for the phase two sustaining period, thus integrating the whole process and enormously increasing his chance of success. Miracle diets do not do this. They may take weight off quickly, but the subsequent attempt to return to "normal eating" becomes, in effect, a confrontation with an unfamiliar food situation and leads to overeating and return of weight.

Now—why slow dieting and slow weight loss? First, a mixed, low-calorie diet as described above must be slow—that is, dieting cannot be too stringent because, if it is, hunger will ensue. And hunger is an enemy most fat people cannot cope with.

124

Therefore, low calorie does not mean too low. In most cases, it means low enough to guarantee between a pound- and two-pound weight loss a week—no more than that, however tempted one may be to eat less.

Losing weight slowly serves another extremely important purpose. It gives the fat person a chance to adjust his new physical dimensions to his new image. I'll have more to say about adjustments in a later insight, but I do want to say here that adjustment takes time. If physical change takes place too fast, the fat person feels as if his body is not his own. "I feel as if I'm living in an empty sack." This "empty sack" feeling brings on anxiety, depression, and a return to free eating. Free eating is something the fat man cannot do if he is to sustain thinness. He can eat more once his weight loss is complete—and he should eat more in order to stop losing weight—but he cannot eat freely. Once he gets used to a limited maintenance diet and eats within those limits automatically, almost without self-consciousness, he will feel far freer, even though food intake will be limited.

Thinning in its second—or lifelong—phase requires compassionate and realistic limitations. Once he arrives at his goal, the formerly heavy person simply cannot go back to eating in the quantities he consumed at his heavy weight. A thinner, lighter body requires less food, and an increase in food leads immediately to weight gain. Indeed, you can eat more food in sustaining a heavy body weight, because more weight requires more food to metabolize in order to sustain it. The "empty sack" feeling is best prevented by losing weight as slowly as possible. Sometimes this even helps physically, giving the skin and muscles time to readjust to new dimensions. But, more important, it gives the fat man or woman a chance to adjust emotionally to the change in body size as it occurs—a chance to experience as little onslaught to his sense of identity as possible. Remember, when one's identity is threatened, anxiety follows. And the formerly fat person inevitably responds to this anxiety with a counterattack of great and voluminous eating as his fastest and most familiar defense. This response initiates the return to a fat body, an old, comfortable because familiar, identifying structure.

But—we are not automatons, and most of us have a long history of binges. Even at our best we must expect lapses in dieting. These lapses are sometimes displaced attacks of anger. Often they are "attacks of abandon." When these lapses occur, self-chastisement is absolutely ruled out and must be guarded against and stopped as soon as it is recognized. Every attempt must be made to prevent any kind of self-deprecation. It must be remembered that self-hate invariably leads to wilder and more chronic binges; in some cases, if people are sufficiently disappointed with themselves, it can become one long, endless binge. Compassion for self is definitely in order during difficult diet times. If we can discover that we are in fact angry or anxious or both, so much the better. If we can find out what it is that is making us feel that way, this insight will help us to know ourselves better, to grow emotionally, while at the same time, it will give us the power to limit the binge and help us cut down the frequency of future binges. If we find that we really miss and require a feeling of abandon, we must find still other areas where it is possible. During a self-hating attack, we are incapable of these insights about ourselves. They are made possible only by treating ourselves with kindness, whether the dieting temporarily goes well or ill!

10.

Sound, Sight, Taste, Smell, and Imagination

To help *controlled eating*—and that's what diet-ing, both to lose and to sustain weight loss really is—fat people must remember that they have very sharp, receptive, and reactive senses.

Of course, as I described in *Forever Thin*, mouth-oriented people are particularly susceptible to the taste and sensation of food, in or near the mouth, and respond accordingly. But they must also be wary of other senses too, because their enormously vital senses make them particularly vulnerable to temptation and surrender. This strong sensitivity coupled with a superb imagination (and many fat people have that, too) makes for formidable eating attacks which are difficult to ward off. To be fore-warned here can be very helpful, and it is interesting that so many fat people do not realize that just about all of their senses play a large role in their succumbing to temptation. Some in fact do realize it, but are too pompous to admit lack of control. Others realize it and go out of their way to avoid stimuli to their senses or imaginations. Some manage to be particularly careful when in their presence.

I remember one man who would immediately fantasize splendid imaginary feasts if he so much as saw a cooking utensil or a nicely set table. Sometimes he fantasized food when he saw vague and indistinct objects from a distance. Seeing other people eating heartily, especially fat people, was usually much more than he could withstand.

One woman I know used to salivate when she heard kitchen sounds and especially the sound of dishes being changed, or what she imagined as the sound of food frying. If she thought she heard other people eating, her own appetite was immediately stimulated. She had already tried and failed in a course of hynopsis and behavioral modification. I don't care for those approaches. I have little faith in processes in which people are not fully conscious participants in their own lives, and I don't like any kind of "treatment" on a symptomatic level. Eventually, she was helped by gaining insight into herself and her responses. Strange as it seems, she did not at first realize that there was a connection between the sounds of food being prepared and eaten and the stimulation of her appetite. Later on she made other

130

important connections which were more helpful. She recalled that some of the most colorful moments in her childhood took place in an active, noisy kitchen. As she became aware of her unconscious attempt to recreate those happy times, she became less subject to her response to food sounds. But even before she became aware of childhood associations and connections, knowing about her automatic response and being prepared for it was helpful.

The strongest temptation and response is, I believe, provoked by the smell of food. A good food aroma is almost irresistible to nearly all fat people. Some bakers know this and that the smell of cake baked in plenty of butter is powerful. Chocolate smells for some are another potent lure, as are frankfurter smells for others—for many of us, just about any cooking odor lures. True thins may find cooking odors revolting, but not us. Our sense of smell is not nearly so strong as that found in other species, but it is strong enough to make food irresistible. Yes, I believe that it is very important to fully know—and I have known any number of people who even under full attack really did not know—that smell probably produces the most direct and strongest temptation of all.

11.

Hopelessness and Resignation

A sense of hopelessness in fat people who desire to be thin comes from a desire for instant gratification in terms of goals. If weight loss isn't forthcoming immediately and perceptibly, hopelessness often follows, despite the dieter's insight into the value of slow dieting and gradual loss. This hopelessness is usually minor and transient, and if *consciously* linked to impatience, disappears without permanently damaging the cause. Impatience is far more destructive if you are not conscious of the fact that you are impatient and frustrated because you are also not fully conscious of your demand for instant results. Lack of consciousness of the difficulty makes it impossible to struggle and overcome the very difficulty which continues from its hidden position to undermine constructive action. Hopelessness can also become pervasive and chronic, and can lead to resignation and surrender of the weight loss project. This usually occurs if the fat person has not fully resolved the conflict described earlier, and still wants all the joys inherent in free eating, while at the same time wanting to lose weight and sustain that loss. Conflict cannot be resolved without surrender—in this case giving up free eating—and the refusal to give up one aspect of the conflict leads to chronic hopelessness. This is so because it is indeed contradictory and impossible to lose weight while eating enough to gain weight. Resignation resulting from hopelessness due to wanting *both* weight loss and free eating at the same time leads either to abject surrender so that weight loss becomes a dead issue or to repeated and abortive attempts to "do it." These repeated attempts are doomed to failure from the start, and the victim usually knows it, even while he gives himself pep talks. I believe that chronic efforts ending in repeated failure (usually the "trying period" gets shorter and shorter, and surrender takes place with less and less weight loss) is largely due to this hopelessness and resignation. Strange as it seems, most people do not know on a fully conscious level that they are caught in this bind. They may even joke about it and not fully recognize its impact.

Therefore, when hopelessness begins to pervade your outlook, you must ask whether it is transient

134

and due to impatience or chronic (do you have a history of repeated attacks of hopelessness followed by giving up dieting?) and pervasive. If it is the first, you must ask yourself for *time*. If it is the second, you must make yourself fully aware that the hopelessness lies in your desire to eat freely, diet effectively, and lose weight, all at the same time. Surrendering the joys of free eating requires full and open consent to feel fully the loss of *free eating joy* involved. This is the only way to resolve the conflict and cure malignant hopelessness. Otherwise, you will establish a pattern of resignation and chronic intermittent effort, followed by abject failure, and eventually, a complete withdrawal from future attempts at thinning.

12.

Period of Adjustment

Instant adjustments, just like instant relationships, are not characteristic of human beings. A loss
of weight, especially a large loss involving a profound change in eating habits, requires a period of
adjustment. This takes time and must be expected.
I've indicated earlier that a slow weight loss helps us
get used to change. But further adjustments are necessary, even after weight is lost. For my purposes
here, adjustment includes physical orientation to a
new body outline; acceptance of controlled eating,
which means eating a *comfortable* amount of food
which will sustain weight within a few pounds
without undue gain or loss; emotional adjustment
and any social adjustments which present themselves.

Most of these changes and their individual variations can be handled by understanding the fat condition. But on the subject of emotional and social adjustments I would like to comment on some subtle factors which I feel are relevant and important.

One of the most difficult of these is to *give up the preoccupation with dieting and weight.* This is particularly difficult because fat people must, at best, always live on the frontier of weight gain. They can always put it back on because it is in keeping with the basic stuff of their personality to EAT. (I'll have something to say about putting weight back on in the next insight.) So, to ask the dieter to moderate his weight preoccupation let alone to give it up, while simultaneously cautioning wariness, because the pounds *do* in fact add up, is asking a lot. Yet dilution of preoccupation is desirable because it has a greatly liberating effect on a person and, I believe, eventually enhances self-esteem.

All preoccupations have a demeaning and depleting effect. Being free of them restores energy, spontaneity, and freedom. To do this, however, one must understand the insights I describe thoroughly, one must exercise at least some will power to stop constantly talking, thinking, checking diets and weight, and one must occupy oneself with other areas, preferably those of interest which offer the possibility of healthy growth.

But we must also be patient. Giving up a lifelong preoccupation with weight requires considerable time for readjustment to another outlook. If controlled eating becomes automatic, weight control will eventually be relegated to a routine place on your list of priorities, where, in most cases, it really belongs. *But* this does take time!

If there is a great change in body dimensions, it is possible that our relationships may change, too. Remember that adjustments to new relationships or change in old relationships brought on by a marked change in appearance or new self-confidence require time and patience. Some people cannot tolerate change. They are afraid of anything unfamiliar, including change in either physical image or personality. Some people—friends, lovers, family, colleagues—will become overtly hostile to the dieter in response to their own envy or jealousy. The threat of confrontation with someone with whom they previously felt comfortable because they considered he or she was "handicapped" but whom they now find too "normal," is real. These people need time to readjust to what in effect is now a new relationship. But even given the time, some people cannot make this readjustment and will become chronically and destructively hostile. In these instances, it may well be necessary to terminate some old relationships and concentrate on forming new ones.

Fat people are often very rebellious and sometimes, even without awareness, will eat if they are told not to eat or find themselves in a job that requires thinness. I have seen in consultation quite a number of fat people who went to work for weight reduction groups or airlines. They had fewer difficulties until they took on these jobs. But the coercion to keep thin was too much for them and precipitated rebellion and eating. They were not fully aware of the cause and effect operating here. Awareness in this area can be helpful, but in some cases it is necessary to break coercive relationships socially and/or professionally in order to achieve and sustain weight loss.

I must also point out that fat people do not give up their need to be liked along with the pounds they shed. Sensitivity to rejection continues to be a problem. As I pointed out earlier, some people who used to find them acceptable when they were heavy will reject them when they become thin, even though they now conform to cultural standards. Fat people respond to rejection with anger (often repressed) and bruised feelings. This of course makes them vulnerable to eating binges unless they are prepared for the situation in advance.

Fat people who have just become thin must exercise compassionate patience with themselves. Even if all aspects of one's fat soul have been retained, new physical dimensions, new and different clothes, changes in relationships, changes in food habits, and confrontations with anxiety-producing situations without the defense of free eating—*all* make for a changed sense of self and require time, patience, and being as good to oneself as possible.

140

13.

How Other People See Us

This insight is corollary to number 12, but I consider it important enough to deserve its own place.

Many of us measure our weight by how we think *other* people see us. Not only do we distort our impressions of how other people see us, but most other people are as highly subjective in how they see us. This then makes for distortions of distortions and has little to do with objective, let alone constructive reality. Other people see us with eyes clouded by their own prejudices and distortions. They see us relative to how often they see us, when they saw us last, what our weight was at that time, how they feel about their own weight, how they feel about us generally, how they respond to fatness and thinness, and so on.

We often, without conscious awareness, seek out those people who see us as thinner or fatter, according to our needs at a particular time. We also project our own needs to certain people who we know will consistently pick up what we want to hear from them at a given time and who will faithfully and reliably comply. Of course, observations, admonitions, and standards set by other people (and often manipulated by ourselves and strained through the others for further distortion) will have little or nothing to do with constructive reality.

It is, therefore, of vital importance not to base one's decisions about weight or evaluate one's weight loss, one way or the other, on the basis of other people's opinions. This is particularly true after weight is lost when some people will inevitably say, "You are much too thin" or others will still ask, "Have you thought of losing a few pounds?" To evaluate yourself on the basis of others, is taking the direct route into emotional quicksand. More often than not you are depriving yourself of a sense of accomplishment and sometimes demoralizing yourself, or even destroying months of hard work and struggle.

I wrote in *The Thin Book by a Formerly Fat Psychiatrist* that if you can't do it for yourself, you may be able to do it for loved ones. In retrospect I feel that this rarely works. It is infinitely better to do something if you want to do it, for yourself. Whatever the particular motivations, they are usually only effective if they are your very own. This is true of all difficult struggles and thinning *is* a difficult struggle. We do best when the center of our lives is lodged in our own substance, rather than in the hands of other people. We do best when we are in charge of our own lives and this is particularly true when we choose to stand up and oppose any cultural values which we feel ultimately lead to self-hate. If and when we capitulate to cultural standards—if and when we choose to take off some pounds—whatever the reason, we must be particularly careful to retain our autonomy. It is self-enhancing and ultimately serves our purpose best if we decide to lose weight for ourselves, evaluate the result for ourselves, and keep thin for ourselves.

14.

Settling

There is nothing wrong with "settling." A strategic retreat does not represent a failure. Indeed, it can well be the makings of continued success.

If it becomes apparent that the goal which was set cannot be reached, it is most important to avoid self-hate which will lead inevitably to a binge. If the goal has been reached but cannot be maintained, despite repeated attempts, again it is vital to our interest to retain maximum compassion for ourselves. But it is also of great importance and value at this point to reassess the goal and, if necessary, to settle for a smaller weight loss. This settling and retrenching is often the most constructive thing we can do to save the situation and ensure that we come out considerably ahead of the game, instead of losing it altogether.

Considering healthy vitality, normal appetite, and the habits of a lifetime, weight that is too low is untenable. This conclusion—that a particular weight is either impossible to attain, or once attained, not possible to sustain—is usually determined by the simple process of trial and error. Since a very thin body requires less food than a heavier one to sustain its weight, that same body takes only a little extra eating to put on weight. That little extra may, however, be the minimum necessary to a fat person's emotional well-being. Arriving at a comfortable amount of food consumption is as important as arriving at a comfortable weight. Both must be compatible with each other and with the psychological needs of the dieter. If discomfort is profound and prolonged, a disastrous chronic binge will follow. Therefore, recognition of comfortable levels is vital and settling for a comfortably compatible level can save the day!

Sometimes, after considerable time at a new weight level has passed, it is easier to bring your weight down another increment, even to the original goal desired. Having gotten used to eating less over a period of time, you may then possess the psychological and physiological outlook favorable both to further weight loss and to sustaining that loss. This frame of mind might well have been impossible if weight loss had been attempted in one uninterrupted leap downward. This is often the case because prolonged deprivation is too much for most fat people to take without rebellion and a subsequent eating binge.

You must be equally wary of a phenomenon I call *shifting goals*. This happens when the dieter shifts his weight goals lower each time he reaches his previous goal. This is especially likely to happen if weight loss is arrived at ahead of schedule or if dieting has been too stringent. Shifting goals is a fooler! It invariably leads to increasing dissatisfaction with your weight, however low it gets, until you arrive at a weight which is impossible to sustain. This leads to dissatisfaction with any realistic level of loss and especially with the original weight goal. "How can I settle for *that*—I've already gotten *way* below that at one time?" This, then, is a malignant version of working with an inappropriate standard and is the antithesis of prudent settling. Shifting goals reminds me of the surgeon who operates for one condition, opens the belly, and finds several other conditions. He keeps on operating for hours and hours, forgetting his original goal, and causing the patient to die from an insupportable surgical onslaught.

15.

The Comfort Paradox

It is comforting to keep in mind that we can if we choose put the weight back. When I first tell patients that they are always free to put weight back on they look at me as if I'm either crazy, caustically sarcastic, or even a potential enemy. None of this is true, and I say this not only in friendship, but as a very important and constructive truth! Choices and decisions can be altered without self-hate. This is not true of obsessive contracts which are irrevocable and whose rupture is always followed by intense self-hate (usually in the form of gaining more weight than you have originally lost). The comfort paradox does more than give comfort. It reduces anxiety and thus aids the cause immeasurably, because it offers an "out" if desired. In effect it sustains psychological (and physical) freedom of movement.

Simply stated the comfort paradox is—knowing and giving ourselves the right to put the weight back helps to keep it off. It is very important to reiterate this truth to yourself periodically. Keeping your options open sets you free, and continuing freedom reduces sensitivity to coercion and the sense of being irrevocably locked in.

The comfort paradox is the antithesis of the anxiety-producing, tyrannical contract and is most effective in diluting and negating destructive and compulsive rebelliousness which takes the form of chronic eating binges. Rebelliousness is, after all, largely a reaction to lack of freedom of choice. When it comes to controlled eating, as in all other areas of living, it is important periodically to renew your right to freely reevaluate your options and to make new choices. This is largely the basis of sustaining alive spontaneity and is the antithesis of directed, wooden, deadened, mechanical behavior.

HELP!

Some of us cannot do it alone, but nevertheless we want to thin. This is no reason either for resigned surrender or self-derision. Indeed, self-derision and self-hate prevent effective help. Enormous pride in doing it alone leads to massive self-recrimination in the rare cases where we seek outside help despite inner admonitions against the move. It is therefore important and really represents an additional insight to openly confront the issue if it exists. This kind of sick pride must be brought to the surface and vanquished if forthcoming help is to be effective.

If this proud resistance to help is repressed, visits to doctors will inevitably be followed by enormous eating and weight gain. Yes, it is imperative that we not only give ourselves permission to get help, with-

151

out feeling embarrassed or put down by it, but that we actually *appreciate ourselves* and allow ourselves to experience the renewed self-esteem that comes with *giving* ourselves needed help. This is the anti-pride, compassionate position and is of great importance whenever self-hate is repressed, but nevertheless lies in wait to sabotage effort.

The help group I like best is Overeaters Anonymous. While I don't hold with their concept of a "higher power"—because I feel that responsibility for thinning ought to be lodged in the center of the self—I like their openness and honesty. They are extremely supportive, nonjudgmental, and generally accepting. I like the fact that they are not a business. They are a nonprofit organization.

May I point out that I still feel that no group or physician (except in cases of gross obesity or physical pathology) ought to determine weight standards. This is an individual matter which is best determined by the individual, even when outside help is sought. This is the best guarantee against falling prey to cultural pressure and prejudice. Outside help, therefore, does not mean placing your life and responsibility for standards and goals in somebody else's hands. These must be retained by the fat person who, hopefully, will understand and retain the virtues of fatness even as he gets thin. Of course, caution must be exercised against pill pushers, charlatans, chicanery, and even well-meaning experts. *But* caution must particularly be exercised against

Thinning

sadistic "helpers," pressuring "helpers," and prejudiced "helpers." If a person finds that he or she has been seeking help from a person who doesn't *like* fat people, that relationship is best terminated at once!

Psychotherapeutic groups run by nonprofit psychotherapeutic clinics (like the one at the Karen Horney Psychoanalytic Clinic) can be very valuable. *But* here too the therapist who leads the group is very important, and the question of prejudice is particularly pertinent here. The group therapist *must be without fat prejudice* in order to prevent absolutely any sadistic onslaughts by one group member on another. Sadism, manipulation, heavy and aggressive admonitions to lose weight either go nowhere or lead to all sorts of emotional disaster.

Some people need an outside authority figure to relate to and to communicate with, in order to engage successfully in the weight loss process. It is helpful if that person is medically expert in weight control as well as in matters psychological. But it is absolutely necessary that he or she be *benevolent and objective and in no way despotic or exploitative.* A doctor who knows his business and who is objective and benevolent is excellent for this purpose, because he will never impose his own difficulties on the patient. There are some internists interested in weight reduction and nutrition who fit this bill. Those I've met were not specialists in weight control.

153

Psychoanalytic psychotherapy is the best method of all in undermining compulsive-obsessive activity. Unlike behavior modification, the concerns of analysis are largely with the dynamics underlying and causing the symptoms, rather than with symptoms themselves.

It is not only a more profound mode of treatment but one concerned with putting the individual at the center of his own life. Psychoanalysis involves self-acceptance and compassion for self, insights involving self, self-responsibility, increasing tolerance of frustration and anxiety, reduction of anxiety and thereby reduction of symptoms and defenses (gross overeating) that are a function of anxiety, resolution of conflicts, more constructive handling of emotions, especially anger, increased understanding of relating to other people, and all aspects of constructive maturation. Psychoanalysis is, therefore, the antithesis of treatment of the individual on a passive, conditioned-reflex basis. It involves the patient actively and calls upon him or her to struggle heroically and constructively against all self-hating devices developed in his lifetime. Psychoanalytic psychotherapy is, from my point of view, primarily helpful as applied to the totality of being a human being. In psychoanalytic treatment, the analyst concerns himself with the entire person and, indeed, must not in any way focus on the patient's weight. Indeed, weight and diet may not be discussed directly in many cases. Weight control is a secondary benefit, a side benefit, if you will, the primary purpose of analysis being self-realization in all areas of living. I feel that psychoanalytic treatment by physicians qualified to do this work is always indicated for people who are grossly overweight and suffer from chronic, obsessive-compulsive, severe (self-imposed but uncontrollable) overeating. They cannot give up the symptom without getting at the cause. It is also dangerous to get rid of the symptom which acts as a defense against severe anxiety, without reducing that anxiety. It is not necessary that the psychoanalyst be fat himself, or that he be particularly interested in problems of obesity. But it helps. There are a handful of therapists who are particularly interested in weight control, some of whom are fat themselves. I feel that they share a kind of common language and mutuality with fat patients which aids the analytic process. Also, I must admit that I am prejudiced in favor of fat people, and this includes therapists who are fat, too.

I am a psychoanalyst and I too believe that self-acceptance is much more important than weight loss. I also believe that fat people must stand up against cultural pressures and in so doing promote acceptance of themselves. Weight loss must be based on personal choice if it is to be successful and constructive. Personality assets characteristic of fat people must not be surrendered or aberrated as a sacrifice to getting and staying thin. Natural proclivities, vitality, and health must be sustained. Thinning must be a benevolent and compassionate process, otherwise it is not thinning at all, but rather destructive, obsessive dieting. Let me quote from *Book of Beauty* by Diane von Furstenberg (Simon and Schuster, March, 1977) which illustrates this point: "I think too thin is also unattractive for any woman, even a young woman. I had a friend whom I considered very attractive. So did an awful lot of people, including many men. Last year she went to work for a high-fashion designer and got carried away with the idea of wearing his clothes. She became involved with her new 'image' and got very, very thin. When I saw her again after a few months I was shocked. She was so thin, all bony. Her face was gaunt, just hollows. She was very fashionable—but she was no longer an attractive, desirable woman. It's more important to be healthy and of good spirits than it is to be thin . . ."

We must entitle ourselves to be fat and alive in America—either with heavy or lighter bodies—but *as we choose.*